PEARSON LONGMAN KEYSTONE

A

PEARSON English Learning System

Workbook

Ben Gordon

Anna Uhl Chamot

John De Mado

Sharroky Hollie

PEARSON

Upper Saddle River, New Jersey • Boston, Massachusetts • Chandler, Arizona • Glenview, Illinois

PEARSON English Learning System

Workbook

Staff credits: The people who made up the Longman Keystone team, representing editorial, production, design, manufacturing, and marketing, are John Ade, Rhea Banker, Liz Barker, Danielle Belfiore, Virginia Bernard, Kenna Bourke, Anne Boynton-Trigg, Johnnie Farmer, Patrice Fraccio, Geraldine Geniusas, Charles Green, Henry Hild, Lucille M. Kennedy, Ed Lamprich, Emily Lippincott, Tara Maceyak, Maria Pia Marrella, Linda Moser, Laurie Neaman, Sherri Pemberton, Liza Pleva, Edie Pullman, Tania Saiz-Sousa, Chris Siley, Lynn Sobotta, Heather St. Clair, Jennifer Stem, Jane Townsend, Marian Wassner, Lauren Weidenman, and Adina Zoltan.

Smithsonian American Art Museum contributors: Project director and writer: Elizabeth K. Eder, Ph.D.; Writer: Mary Collins; Image research assistants: Laurel Fehrenbach, Katherine G. Stilwill, and Sally Otis; Rights and reproductions: Richard H. Sorensen and Leslie G. Green; Building photograph by Tim Hursley.

Cover Image: Background, John Foxx/Getty Images; Inset, Stockbyte/Getty Images
Text composition: TSI Graphics
Text font: 11 pt ITC Stone Sans Std
Photos: 20, right, Art Wolfe/Stone Allstock/Getty Images; 20, left, Adam Woolfitt/CORBIS; 48, Andy Crawford/Dorling Kindersley; 220, David A. Hardy/Photo Researchers, Inc.
Technical art: TSI Graphics

ISBN-13: 978-1-4284-3504-9
ISBN-10: 1-4284-3504-2

Printed in the United States of America
12V0N4 16 15

Contents

Unit 1

READING 1

Vocabulary: Key Words . . . 1
Vocabulary: Academic Words . . . 2
Word Study: Same Sound, Different Spellings . . . 3
Reading Strategy: Preview . . . 4
Comprehension . . . 5
Extension . . . 5
Grammar: Parts of Speech and Parts of the Sentence . . . 6
Writing: Describe a Place . . . 8

READING 2

Vocabulary: Literary Words . . . 9
Vocabulary: Academic Words . . . 10
Word Study: Compound Nouns . . . 11
Reading Strategy: Draw Conclusions . . . 12
Comprehension . . . 13
Response to Literature . . . 13
Grammar: Possessive Nouns, Adjectives, and Pronouns; Indefinite Pronouns . . . 14
Writing: Describe an Event . . . 16

READING 3

Vocabulary: Key Words . . . 17
Vocabulary: Academic Words . . . 18
Word Study: Spellings Words with *ai, ay, ee,* and *oa* . . . 19
Reading Strategy: Use Visuals 1 . . . 20
Comprehension . . . 21
Extension . . . 21
Grammar: Comparison Structures: Comparative and Superlative Adjectives . . . 22
Writing: Describe an Object . . . 24

READING 4

Vocabulary: Literary Words . . . 25
Vocabulary: Academic Words . . . 26
Word Study: Prefixes *un-, dis-* . . . 27
Reading Strategy: Predict . . . 28
Comprehension . . . 29
Response to Literature . . . 29
Grammar: Single-Word and Multi-Word Prepositions of Location . . . 30
Writing: Write a Description of a Character . . . 32

Writing Workshop . . . 33
Learning Log . . . 34
Test Preparation . . . 35
Learn about Art with the Smithsonian American Art Museum . . . 39

Unit 2

READING 1

Vocabulary: Key Words 41
Vocabulary: Academic Words 42
Word Study: Spelling Words with Long Vowel Sound /ē/ 43
Reading Strategy: Compare and Contrast 44
Comprehension 45
Extension 45
Grammar: Showing Contrast: Coordinating Conjunctions and Conjunctive Adverbs 46
Writing: Write a Friendly Letter 48

READING 2

Vocabulary: Literary Words 49
Vocabulary: Academic Words 50
Word Study: Suffixes *-ness*, *-tion*, and *-ation* 51
Reading Strategy: Visualize 52
Comprehension 53
Response to Literature 53
Grammar: Count and Non-count Nouns; Quantifiers 54
Writing: Write about a Character and Setting 56

READING 3

Vocabulary: Key Words 57
Vocabulary: Academic Words 58
Word Study: Spelling Words with Long-Vowel Sound /ō/ 59
Reading Strategy: Use Visuals 2 60
Comprehension 61
Extension 61
Grammar: Simple Past: Regular and Irregular Verbs 62
Writing: Write a Story from a Different Point of View 64

READING 4

Vocabulary: Literary Words 65
Vocabulary: Academic Words 66
Word Study: Animal Verbs and Idioms 67
Reading Strategy: Recognize Sequence 68
Comprehension 69
Response to Literature 69
Grammar: Direct Quotations: Statements and Questions 70
Writing: Write a Personal Narrative 72

Writing Workshop 73
Learning Log 74
Test Preparation 75
Learn about Art with the Smithsonian American Art Museum 79

Unit 3

READING 1

Vocabulary: Literary Words . . . 81
Vocabulary: Academic Words . . . 82
Word Study: Uses of the Apostrophe . . . 83
Reading Strategy: Make Inferences . . . 84
Comprehension . . . 85
Response to Literature . . . 85
Grammar: Agreement in Simple and Compound Sentences . . . 86
Writing: Write a Book Review . . . 88

READING 2

Vocabulary: Key Words . . . 89
Vocabulary: Academic Words . . . 90
Word Study: Spelling Words with Silent *gh* . . . 91
Reading Strategy: Identify Problems and Solutions . . . 92
Comprehension . . . 93
Extension . . . 93
Grammar: Prepositions of Time; Prepositional Phrases; Providing Details . . . 94
Writing: Write a Persuasive Paragraph . . . 96

READING 3

Vocabulary: Literary Words . . . 97
Vocabulary: Academic Words . . . 98
Word Study: Synonyms and Antonyms . . . 99
Reading Strategy: Distinguish Fact from Fiction . . . 100
Comprehension . . . 101
Response to Literature . . . 101
Grammar: Placement of Adjectives . . . 102
Writing: Write a Diary Entry . . . 104

READING 4

Vocabulary: Key Words . . . 105
Vocabulary: Academic Words . . . 106
Word Study: Greek and Latin Roots . . . 107
Reading Strategy: Identify Main Idea and Details . . . 108
Comprehension . . . 109
Extension . . . 109
Grammar: Participial Adjectives; Prepositions of Location . . . 110
Writing: Write a Critical Evaluation . . . 112

Writing Workshop . . . 113
Learning Log . . . 114
Test Preparation . . . 115
Learn about Art with the Smithsonian American Art Museum . . . 119

Unit 4

READING 1

Vocabulary: Literary Words 121
Vocabulary: Academic Words 122
Word Study: Spelling Long Vowel Sound /ī/ 123
Reading Strategy: Read for Enjoyment 124
Comprehension 125
Response to Literature 125
Grammar: Present Perfect 126
Writing: Write a Response to Literature 128

READING 2

Vocabulary: Key Words 129
Vocabulary: Academic Words 130
Word Study: Homophones 131
Reading Strategy: Recognize Cause and Effect 132
Comprehension 133
Extension 133
Grammar: Complex Sentences with Subordinating Conjunctions; Subordinating Conjunctions with Adverb Clauses 134
Writing: Write a Cause-and-Effect Paragraph 136

READING 3

Vocabulary: Literary Words 137
Vocabulary: Academic Words 138
Word Study: Spellings for *r*-Controlled Vowels 139
Reading Strategy: Identify Author's Purpose 140
Comprehension 141
Response to Literature 141
Grammar: Adverbs of Manner; Placement of Adverbs of Manner 142
Writing: Write a Compare-and-Contrast Paragraph 144

READING 4

Vocabulary: Key Words 145
Vocabulary: Academic Words 146
Word Study: Multiple–Meaning Words 147
Reading Strategy: Ask Questions 148
Comprehension 149
Extension 149
Grammar: Past Perfect and Simple Past 150
Writing: Write a Newspaper Article 152

Writing Workshop 153
Learning Log 154
Test Preparation 155
Learn about Art with the Smithsonian American Art Museum 159

Unit 5

READING 1

Vocabulary: Literary Words 161
Vocabulary: Academic Words 162
Word Study: Spelling Words with *oo* 163
Reading Strategy: Analyze Text Structure 1 164
Comprehension. 165
Response to Literature 165
Grammar: *Be going to* and *will*; Degrees of Certainty about the Future 166
Writing: Write a Formal E-mail 168

READING 2

Vocabulary: Key Words 169
Vocabulary: Academic Words 170
Word Study: Suffixes *-ic, -ist, -able* 171
Reading Strategy: Follow Steps in a Process. 172
Comprehension. 173
Extension 173
Grammar: Imperatives; Sequence Words and Phrases 174
Writing: Write How-to Instructions 176

READING 3

Vocabulary: Literary Words 177
Vocabulary: Academic Words 178
Word Study: Prefixes *mega-, tele-, re-* 179
Reading Strategy: Summarize. 180
Comprehension. 181
Response to Literature 181
Grammar: Reported Speech: Questions, Imperatives, *told*. 182
Writing: Write a Plot Summary 184

READING 4

Vocabulary: Key Words 185
Vocabulary: Academic Words 186
Word Study: Spelling Words with *ea* 187
Reading Strategy: Classify. 188
Comprehension. 189
Extension 189
Grammar: Active Voice and Passive Voice; Passive Voice: Omitting the *by*-Phrase 190
Writing: Write a Paragraph That Classifies. 192

Writing Workshop. 193
Learning Log 194
Test Preparation. 195
Learn about Art with the Smithsonian American Art Museum 199

Unit 6

READING 1

Vocabulary: Key Words 201
Vocabulary: Academic Words 202
Word Study: Spelling the Diphthongs /oi/ and /ou/ 203
Reading Strategy: Take Notes 204
Comprehension 205
Extension 205
Grammar: Transitions 206
Writing: Write an Introductory Paragraph 208

READING 2

Vocabulary: Literary Words 209
Vocabulary: Academic Words 210
Word Study: Greek and Latin Roots 211
Reading Strategy: Analyze Text Structure 2 212
Comprehension 213
Response to Literature 213
Grammar: General Rules of Capitalization; Capitalization: Abbreviations, Initials, and Special Terms 214
Writing: Support a Main Idea with Examples 216

READING 3

Vocabulary: Literary Words 217
Vocabulary: Academic Words 218
Word Study: Schwa Spelled *a, e, i, o, u* 219
Reading Strategy: Skim 220
Comprehension 221
Response to Literature 221
Grammar: End Punctuation, Commas, and Quotation Marks; Parentheses, Brackets, and Ellipses 222
Writing: Include Quotations and Citations 224

READING 4

Vocabulary: Key Words 225
Vocabulary: Academic Words 226
Word Study: Multiple-Meaning Words 227
Reading Strategy: Make Generalizations 228
Comprehension 229
Extension 229
Grammar: Using Quotation Marks for Exact Words; Quotation Marks: Terms, Expressions, and Titles 230
Writing: Include Paraphrases and Citations 232

Writing Workshop 233
Learning Log 234
Test Preparation 235
Learn about Art with the Smithsonian American Art Museum 239

Name ______________________________ Date ______________

Can all mysteries be solved?

READING 1: "Fact or Fiction?"

VOCABULARY **Key Words** *Use with textbook page 5.*

Write each word in the box next to its definition.

archaeologist	clues	creature	disappeared	fantasy	sacred

Example: ___sacred___: relating to a god or religion and believed to be holy

1. ____________________: an animal, fish, or insect

2. ____________________: someone who learns about ancient civilizations by studying the remains of their graves, buildings, and tools

3. ____________________: stopped existing

4. ____________________: information or objects that can help solve a crime or mystery

5. ____________________: a thing or a situation that is not real, but imagined

Use the words in the box at the top of the page to complete the sentences.

6. A detective looks for ____________________ to solve a mystery.

7. The starfish is a ____________________ that lives in water.

8. Scientists are still trying to decide why the dinosaurs ____________________.

9. Another word for holy is ____________________.

10. I have a dream about becoming a star, but it is just a ____________________.

VOCABULARY **Academic Words** *Use with textbook page 6.*

Read the paragraph below. Pay attention to the underlined academic words.

> Why did the dinosaurs disappear? A recent theory is that dinosaurs were killed when an asteroid hit Earth. An asteroid could create enough dust to block out the sun for a long time, killing the plants on Earth. The dinosaurs would not have had enough food to survive. The asteroid theory is supported by new evidence. Many scientists believe this is the most accurate theory on the disappearance of the dinosaurs.

Write the academic words from the paragraph above next to their correct definitions.

Example: _survive_ : continue to live or exist

1. ________________: facts, objects, or signs that make you believe that something exists or is true
2. ________________: make something exist
3. ________________: correct or exact

Use the academic words from the paragraph above to complete the sentences.

4. You can use computer programs to ________________ drawings on the screen.
5. My watch is very ________________.
6. Some animals can ________________ for a long time without food.
7. Right now, we have no ________________ that there is life on other planets.

Complete the sentences with your own ideas.

Example: The pyramids are evidence that the people of Egypt _knew how to build huge buildings_.

8. If my research is not accurate, my paper will ________________.
9. To survive in a cold climate, I would have to ________________.
10. I want to create a new ________________.

Name ______________________ Date ______________

WORD STUDY Same Sound, Different Spellings

Use with textbook page 7.

REMEMBER The sound /ər/ can be spelled different ways when it comes at the end of a word in an unstressed syllable. It can be spelled *ar* as in *dollar*, *er* as in *pitcher*, or *or* as in *actor*.

Read the words in the box below. Then write each word in the correct column in the chart.

~~nectar~~	tractor	cracker	doctor	collar
silver	winter	color	beggar	

/ər/ spelled ar	/ər/ spelled er	/ər/ spelled or
nectar		

Write the letters that stand for the /ər/ sound in each word below. Then use each word in a sentence of your own. Use a dictionary if you are unsure of a word's meaning.

Example: cedar *ar We have a cedar tree in our backyard.*

1. particular ______________________
2. motor ______________________
3. splinter ______________________
4. finger ______________________
5. summer ______________________
6. splendor ______________________
7. scholar ______________________

READING STRATEGY PREVIEW *Use with textbook page 7.*

REMEMBER You can preview the pictures and headings in a passage to prepare yourself for the information you are about to learn.

Look at the picture, headings, and text. Answer the questions that follow.

A Rainbow of Colors

Try Fruits of Different Colors

You probably know that fruits come in a range of colors. But did you know that different colored fruits provide different nutrients? Nutritionists recommend eating fruit from as many different colors as you can each day.

Red, Green, Blue, and White Fruit

Red fruits include raspberries, red grapes, and watermelon. Greens include green grapes and kiwi fruit. Blueberries are a blue fruit and white peaches are a white fruit.

Fruits come in many colors, and eating a variety of colored fruits is good for you.

1. Circle the title and underline the headings. What do you think the article is about?

____

2. Turn each heading into a question.

____

____

3. Look at the picture and its caption. What does it tell you about the article?

____

4. Set a purpose for reading the article.

____

5. How can the skill of previewing help you to understand a text?

____

____

Name ______________________ Date __________

COMPREHENSION

Use with textbook page 14.

Choose the best answer for each item. Circle the letter of the correct answer.

1. The buildings of Machu Picchu were made of ______.

   a. cement **b.** wood **c.** stone blocks

2. Some people think Stonehenge was built as a huge ______.

   a. calendar **b.** thermometer **c.** ruler

3. Many creatures underwater ______.

   a. are imaginary **b.** remain a mystery to humans **c.** are as big as the Loch Ness monster

4. Some people think the Loch Ness monster is ______.

   a. a truck **b.** a sheep **c.** a fantasy

5. The creature Bigfoot ______.

   a. has supposedly been spotted in more than one country **b.** is half human, half bear **c.** has been proven to be a fake

EXTENSION

Use with textbook page 15.

What was a favorite creature of yours when you were young? Was it real or imaginary? If it was imaginary, did it look like any real creatures? Write the name of the creature at the top of the chart. Find or invent information about it. Use the information to complete the rest of the chart.

Name	
Location	
Description	
Behavior	

GRAMMAR Parts of Speech and Parts of the Sentence

Use with textbook pages 16–17.

REMEMBER A sentence always contains a subject and a predicate. The predicate contains either an action verb or a linking verb. Sometimes an action verb is followed by an object.
Example: I drove the car.
A linking verb can be followed by either a noun or an adjective.
Example: The girl is a student. The house is big.
An adjective describes a noun.
Example: The statue is old.
An adverb describes the action of a sentence.
Example: They opened the tomb *carefully*.
A preposition shows time or location and is followed by a noun or noun phrase.
Example: In 1922, they discovered the tomb.

Circle the linking verbs and underline the action verbs.

1. Cheops was an Egyptian Pharaoh.
2. The Great Sphinx is thousands of years old.
3. Some people became sick after opening the tomb.
4. An explorer found giant footprints in the snow.

Circle the adjectives and underline the adverbs.

5. The stars were sacred to the Egyptians.
6. The Sphinx is a huge statue.
7. Lord Carnarvon died mysteriously.
8. Stonehenge accurately measures the sun's movements.

Circle the prepositions of time and underline the prepositions of location.

9. Machu Pichu is located in the Andes Mountains.
10. It was built in the fifteenth century.
11. They found many large statues on the island.
12. People believe that the yeti is a creature from Tibet.

Name ______________________________ Date ______________

Parts of Speech and Parts of the Sentence *Use with textbook pages 16–17.*

REMEMBER A simple sentence must contain a subject and a verb. The verb must agree in number with the subject. If the subject is singular, then the verb must be singular. If the subject is plural, then the verb must be plural.

Complete the chart with the correct word from the box. Write each word under its part of speech.

found quickly on strange in built explorers beautiful carefully statue they

Noun/Pronoun	Adverb	Adjective	Verb	Preposition

Identify the part of speech in italics (noun, pronoun, adverb, adjective, verb, or preposition).

1. The age of the Sphinx is a *mystery*. Noun
2. Some *ancient* cities were abandoned. ______
3. Tourists *from* all over the world visit Machu Pichu. ______
4. Archeologists *found* wooden tablets. ______
5. *They* didn't know how to read the language. ______
6. The dinosaurs disappeared *suddenly*. ______

Decide if each sentence is correct or not. Correct the mistakes.

	Correct	Incorrect
7. The Pyramids is in Egypt.	☐	☐
8. Tutankhamen was an Egyptian Pharaoh.	☐	☐
9. We doesn't know how to read the language.	☐	☐
10. Different cultures give the creature different names.	☐	☐

WRITING **Describe a Place** *Use with textbook pages 18–19.*

Complete your own pyramid for a paragraph that describes a mysterious place.

Top
Middle
Bottom

Use the Peer Review Checklist below to obtain feedback from your partner. This feedback will help you edit your final draft.

PEER REVIEW CHECKLIST

- ☐ Does the paragraph describe a mysterious place?
- ☐ Are details arranged using spatial order?
- ☐ Does the writer use signal words such as *near* and *far*?
- ☐ Does the writing make the reader want to keep reading?
- ☐ Are all sentences complete?
- ☐ What changes could be made to improve the paragraph?

Name ______________________________ Date ______________

Can all mysteries be solved?

READING 2: "Teenage Detectives"

VOCABULARY **Literary Words** *Use with textbook page 21.*

REMEMBER **Idioms** are expressions that have a different meaning from the words that make them up. **Example:** *Under the weather* means "not feeling well." **Puns** are jokes that use a word with more than one meaning, or words that sound the same but have different meanings.
Example: The magician was so angry he pulled his hare out. (*Hare* is an animal similar to a rabbit. *Hare* sounds like the *hair* that grows on your head.)

The sentences below use either puns or idioms. Put a check mark in the correct column for each one.

Sentence	Pun	Idiom
The dress was very expensive; it cost an arm and a leg.		✔
1. One of these new shoes isn't right.		
2. The show was so funny I nearly split my sides laughing.		
3. At first, I couldn't figure out how to fasten my seatbelt, but then it clicked.		
4. Josh spilled the beans about the surprise party.		
5. She has a real green thumb; plants always grow for her.		

Many idioms include references to animals. Some animal idioms are shown in the web below. Think of at least five more idioms that refer to animals. Write them in the circles. If you can think of more idioms, add more circles.

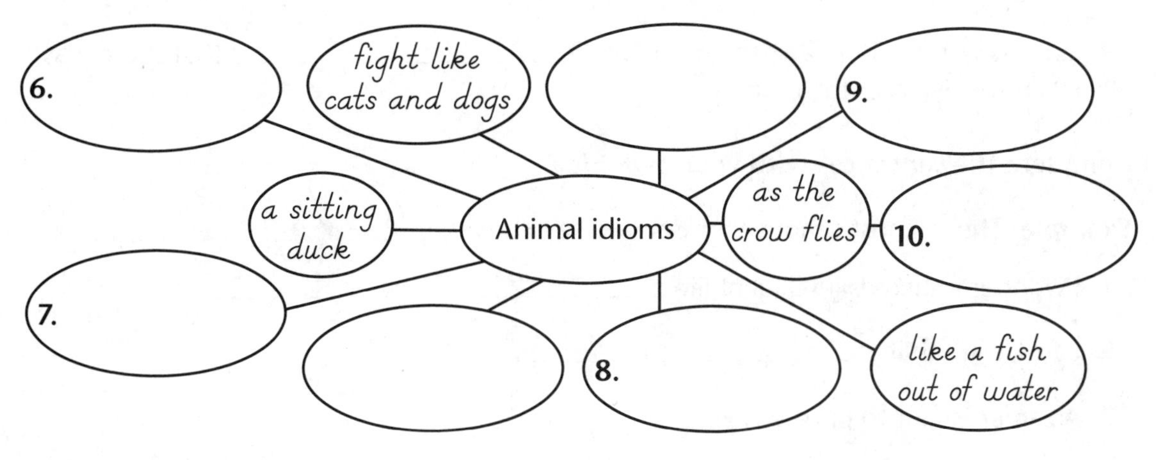

VOCABULARY **Academic Words** *Use with textbook page 22.*

Read the paragraph below. Pay attention to the underlined academic words.

Mysteries are popular because readers like to feel like they are crime solvers. In a mystery novel, a detective tries to solve a crime and <u>pursue</u> a criminal. To do this he must look for clues, and also figure out the <u>motive</u> behind the crime. The criminal is usually very <u>intelligent</u> and makes this difficult. The most exciting part of the story is when the reader becomes <u>aware</u> of all the clues and tries to figure out who the criminal is.

Write the letter of the correct definition next to each word.

Example: ___c___ motive

_____ **1.** pursue

_____ **2.** aware

_____ **3.** intelligent

a. chase or follow someone or something to catch him, her, or it

b. having a high ability to learn, understand, and think about things

c. the reason that makes someone do something, especially when this reason is kept hidden

d. realizing that something is true, exists, or is happening

Use the academic words from the exercise above to complete the sentences.

4. My dog is so ____________________; I think he understands everything I say!

5. Detectives try to find out who had a ____________________ to commit a crime.

6. Some detectives put on a disguise to ____________________ a criminal without being seen.

7. Since it was getting dark, the hikers were not ____________________ that there was a fallen tree lying in the path.

Complete the sentences with your own ideas.

Example: The scientist's motive for doing research was *to find a cure*.

8. I wonder if there is intelligent life ____________________.

9. I am aware that ____________________.

10. A career I want to pursue is ____________________.

Name ______________________________ Date ______________

WORD STUDY Compound Nouns *Use with textbook page 23.*

REMEMBER A compound noun is made up of two or more words. Compound nouns can be written as one word, as in *eyelash*. They can be written as two separate words, as in *web page*. They can be written with a hyphen, as in *father-in-law*. Check the compound noun in a dictionary if you are not sure how to spell it.

Combine the words from the first two columns to form compound nouns. Use a dictionary to find out whether the words are written as one word, as two words, or with a hyphen.

Word 1	Word 2	Compound Noun
book	keeper	*bookkeeper*
air	conditioner	*air conditioner*
great	grandfather	*great-grandfather*
1. light	house	
2. butter	milk	
3. ice	skater	
4. barn	yard	
5. brother	in-law	

Create compound nouns by adding a word from the box to the beginning of each word below. Check your work in a dictionary to see if the compound noun is written as one word, as two words, or with a hyphen.

~~key~~	fire	sea	merry	shoe	apple

Example: ____*key*____ board

6. ______________ -go-round

7. ______________ sauce

8. ______________ lace

9. ______________ shell

10. ______________ drill

READING STRATEGY DRAW CONCLUSIONS

Use with textbook page 23.

REMEMBER To draw conclusions about a text, use clues from the text and your own experience and knowledge to figure out what the author means.

Read the paragraph and answer the questions that follow.

Ella Olensky had just arrived in the Los Angeles airport. America! She couldn't believe she was finally here. As she handed her Russian passport to the officer, she could not help but smile.

1. Where is Ella Olensky from?

____

2. What clues from the text and/or knowledge from your own experience helped you to draw a conclusion about where she is from?

____

____

3. How does Ella Olensky feel about arriving in Los Angeles?

____

____

4. What clues from the text and/or knowledge from your own experience helped you to draw a conclusion about how she feels about arriving in Los Angeles?

____

____

5. How can the skill of drawing conclusions help you to become a better reader?

____

____

Name ______________________________ Date ______________

COMPREHENSION

Use with textbook page 30.

Choose the best answer for each item. Circle the letter of the correct answer.

1. In "The Case of the Defaced Sidewalk," Nina found out who ______.

   a. jumped in wet concrete **b.** had wide feet **c.** needed new shoes

2. Max's mom wants to know what happened at the house because ______.

   a. she knows who lives there **b.** she used to live there **c.** she is the real estate agent

3. The missing signs in "The Case of the Disappearing Signs" were ______.

   a. FOR SALE signs **b.** street signs **c.** stop signs

4. The biggest clue in "The Case of the Disappearing Signs" was ______.

   a. a pickup truck **b.** a fire in July **c.** a lawnmower

5. To figure things out, Max and Nina look for ______.

   a. a magnifying glass **b.** clues **c.** fireplaces

RESPONSE TO LITERATURE

Use with textbook page 31.

Find a paragraph that you like very much in the story. Draw a picture illustrating the images the paragraph presents. Write in dialogue for the people in the picture.

GRAMMAR Possessive Nouns, Adjectives, and Pronouns

Use with textbook page 32.

REMEMBER An apostrophe (') and an *-s* are used to make possessive nouns.
Example: She is Max's Mom.
There are different rules for forming possessive nouns. Add *'s* to singular nouns and irregular plurals. Add ' to plurals ending in *s*. A proper noun ending in *s* can take *'s* or *s'*.

Add an apostrophe to the correct place in each sentence.

1. Nina was eating pizza at Maxs house.
2. The realtors sign was missing.
3. The childrens Mom was confused.
4. They looked at all the neighbors houses.
5. They knocked on Mrs. Stearnss door.
6. They looked in Freddies garage.

Circle the possessive adjective. Underline the possessive pronoun.

7. That truck is mine.
8. Is this your garage?
9. Where is our sign?
10. Their house is for sale.

Circle the correct word to complete each sentence.

11. That is (mine / my) sign. The sign is (my / mine).
12. Is this car (your / yours)? I thought it was (their / theirs).
13. (Our / Ours) house is new, but (your / yours) is old.
14. That's (his / hers) truck. It isn't (hers / their).

Name ________________________________ Date ____________

Indefinite Pronouns *Use with textbook page 33.*

> **REMEMBER** Indefinite pronouns begin with *every-*, *some-*, *any-*, or *no-*. They do not name a specific person, place, or thing.
> **Example:** Why would *anyone* steal a realtor's signs?
> Use a singular pronoun to refer to an indefinite pronoun. In spoken language, you can use a plural pronoun to refer to an indefinite pronoun.

Complete the sentences below with *-one, -body,* or *-thing.*

1. No ________________ knew what happened to the signs.
2. He asked if they knew any ________________ about the house for sale.
3. They couldn't see any ________________ in the garage.
4. They asked every ________________ about the mystery.
5. She didn't want any ________________ moving in next door.
6. We didn't see any ________________ strange in the neighborhood.

Decide if each sentence is correct or not. Correct the mistakes.

	Correct	Incorrect
7. No one know the answer to the puzzle.	☐	☐
8. Someone left theirs footprints in the drive.	☐	☐
9. No one noticed nothing in the street.	☐	☐
10. Everyone have an opinion about it.	☐	☐
11. Someone was waiting in the street.	☐	☐
12. I didn't see no one take the sign.	☐	☐

WRITING **Describe an Event** *Use with textbook pages 34–35.*

Complete your own sequence chart for a paragraph about a made-up event.

Use the Peer Review Checklist below to obtain feedback from your partner. This feedback will help you edit your final draft.

PEER REVIEW CHECKLIST

- ☐ Does the paragraph describe a puzzling event?
- ☐ Does it include humor, puns, or idioms?
- ☐ Does it present what happened in time order?
- ☐ Does the writer use signal words such as *first* and *next*?
- ☐ Is the possessive case used correctly?
- ☐ What changes could be made to improve the paragraph?

Name ______________________________ Date ______________

Can all mysteries be solved?

READING 3: From *G Is for Googol*

VOCABULARY **Key Words** *Use with textbook page 37.*

Write each word in the box next to its definition.

architecture	gradual	infinity	numerals	spirals	steep

Example: ___architecture___: the style and design of buildings

1. ______________: happening or changing slowly over a long time
2. ______________: rising or falling sharply
3. ______________: written signs that represent numbers
4. ______________: shapes that curve around and around as they go up
5. ______________: space or distance that has no limits or end

Use the words in the box at the top of the page to complete the sentences.

6. Long ago, people in Europe used Roman ______________ to write numbers.
7. There was a slow, ______________ change in the temperature from hot to cold.
8. In modern ______________, buildings are often made of concrete, steel, and glass.
9. The path was level at first, but it grew ______________ as we climbed the hill.
10. Many flowers grow in ______________, curving out from the center.

VOCABULARY **Academic Words** *Use with textbook page 38.*

Read the paragraph below. Pay attention to the underlined academic words.

I found a very unique book in the library. It's a book on how to grow carnivorous plants—plants that eat insects. The book uses photographs to illustrate the sequence of steps you need to follow to grow and care for the plants. And because you'll need a constant supply of insects for your plants, the book also tells how to attract and catch flies!

Write the letter of the correct definition next to each word.

Example: ___b___ constant

_____ **1.** illustrate

_____ **2.** sequence

_____ **3.** unique

a. the only one of its type

b. happening regularly or all the time

c. explain or make something clear by giving examples

d. a series of related events, actions, or numbers that have a particular order

Use the academic words from the exercise above to complete the sentences.

4. My teacher will ____________________ an event in history by describing other events like it.

5. Every person has a ____________________ fingerprint.

6. The ____________________ noise in the city gave me a headache.

7. Do you remember the ____________________ of events in the story?

Complete the sentences with your own ideas.

Example: Every snowflake has a unique ______pattern______.

8. It is good to drive at a constant ______________________________.

9. I like to illustrate my ideas by ______________________________.

10. There is a particular sequence of steps to ______________________________.

Name ______________________ Date ____________

WORD STUDY Spelling Words with *ai, ay, ee,* and *oa*

Use with textbook page 39.

REMEMBER Vowel digraphs, or vowel teams, are two letters that work as a team to stand for one vowel sound. For example in the word *goat*, the digraph *oa* stands for one sound: the /ō/ sound. The digraphs *ai, ay, ee,* or *oa* often stand for a long vowel sound, usually the sound of the first letter. Remember this rhyme: "When two vowels go walking, the first one does the talking." For example, the digraph *ai* in *mail* stands for /ā/.

Read the words in the box below quietly to yourself. Listen for the long vowel sound. Then sort the words according to the long vowel sound and its spelling. Write each word in the correct column in the chart.

~~sail~~	straight	coast	disagree	Wednesday	roast
raise	goat	bleed	portray	queen	delay

/ā/ spelled ai	/ā/ spelled ay	/ē/ spelled ee	/ō/ spelled oa
sail			

Circle the vowel digraph that stands for a long vowel sound in each word below. Then use each word in a sentence of your own.

Example: r(oa)d *We drove down a long and bumpy dirt road.*

1. paycheck ____________________
2. steel ____________________
3. afraid ____________________
4. toad ____________________
5. stain ____________________
6. yesterday ____________________
7. weekend ____________________
8. wait ____________________
9. boast ____________________

READING STRATEGY **USE VISUALS 1** *Use with textbook page 39.*

REMEMBER Visuals are the pictures, charts, graphs, maps, and diagrams that can come with a text. You can use visuals in a text to learn more about the topic.

Look at the pictures, chart, and text. Answer the questions that follow.

The Mysteries of Stonehenge and Easter Island

Mysterious Statues

Easter Island is a small island, thousands of miles off the coast of Chile. When explorers reached the island, they found almost 900 statues of figures. Researchers believe that these may have been statues of gods.

Distance that the stones were carried

Monument	Distance
Stonehenge	480 km/300 miles
Easter Island	23 km/14 miles

A Puzzling Monument

Stonehenge in England is a series of big stones arranged in a circle. The monument was built 5,000 years ago, and some believe it was created to measure the sun's movement. But without information from the people who built it, no one can be sure.

1. Underline the title and circle the headings. What do you think the article will be about?

____

2. Draw an *x* over any pictures. How does the picture help you to understand the text?

____

3. Circle the table. How does the table help you to understand the text?

____

4. In one sentence, summarize the article.

____

5. How do you think using visuals can help you to understand a text?

____

Name ______________________________ Date ____________

COMPREHENSION

Use with textbook page 44.

Choose the best answer for each item. Circle the letter of the correct answer.

1. You find the next number in the Fibonacci sequence by _____.

   a. adding the previous two **b.** subtracting the previous two **c.** dividing the last one by two

2. Because of Fibonacci, we now use _____.

   a. Italian numerals **b.** Roman numerals **c.** Arabic numerals

3. The bracts, or knobby parts, of pinecones grow in _____.

   a. straight lines **b.** squares **c.** spirals

4. The Fibonacci sequence is a special _____.

   a. way to do things **b.** number pattern **c.** type of plant

5. Fibonacci numbers are often found in _____.

   a. nature **b.** water **c.** the air

EXTENSION

Use with textbook page 45.

Draw a picture of a new plant or flower. Imagine that you discovered it in the wild, so you must name it. As you draw it, make sure it has patterns. It may have a certain number of blooms or leaves or a certain number of designs in it. Label the patterns.

GRAMMAR Comparison Structures: Comparative Adjectives

Use with textbook page 46.

REMEMBER A comparative adjective describes how two things are the same or different. There are different rules for forming comparative adjectives. For adjectives ending in *-e*, just add *-r*.
Example: large → larger.
With some adjectives, the last letter is doubled before *-er* is added.
Example: big → bigger.
For an adjective ending in *-y*, change *y* to *i* and add *-er*
Example: silly → sillier.
For adjectives with more than two syllables, use more before the adjectives.
Example: exciting → more exciting.

Write the adjectives from the box in the correct place in the chart.

large	big	small	tiny	beautiful	funny	amazing	old	easy	deep	thin	wide

Add *-er*	Add *-r*	Change *y* to *i*, add *-er*	Double consonant, add *-er*	Use *more* + adjective

Complete each sentence below with the comparative form of the adjective in parentheses.

1. Arabic numbers are ____________________ (easy) than Roman numerals.
2. A book about Fibonacci numbers would be ____________________ (heavy) than this book.
3. Nature is ____________________ (amazing) than we realize.
4. Some pinecones are ____________________ (large) than others.
5. The Atlantic Ocean is ____________________ (cold) than the Pacific Ocean.
6. The moon is ____________________(close) to the earth than the sun.

Name ______________________ Date ____________

Comparison Structures: Superlative Adjectives *Use with textbook page 47.*

REMEMBER Superlative adjectives compare one part of a whole group to the rest of that group. There are different rules for forming superlative adjectives.
For adjectives ending in *-e*, just add *-st*. **Example:** large → largest.
With some adjectives, the last letter is doubled before *-est* is added. **Example:** big → biggest.
For an adjective ending in *-y*, change *y* to *i* and add *-est*. **Example:** silly → silliest.
For adjectives with more than two syllables, use *most* before the adjective.
Example: exciting → most exciting. Always use *the* before a superlative.

Complete the chart with the superlative forms of the adjectives.

adjective	superlative	adjective	superlative
thin	*thinnest*	pretty	
smooth		wide	
rough		close	
good		bad	

Complete each sentence below with the superlative form of the adjective in parentheses.

1. What is the ______________ (hot) place on Earth?
2. What is the ______________ (dry) place on Earth?
3. What is the ______________ (large) desert?
4. What is the ______________ (high) mountain?
5. What is the ______________ (deep) ocean?
6. What is the ______________ (populated) city?

Write three more questions about places on Earth. Use any of these adjectives and nouns.

cold dangerous tiny wet crowded big tall wide long	city country river mountain volcano ocean lake waterfall

7. ______________________________?
8. ______________________________?
9. ______________________________?

WRITING Describe an Object *Use with textbook pages 48–49.*

Complete your own word web for a paragraph describing a fruit or vegetable. Include sensory details.

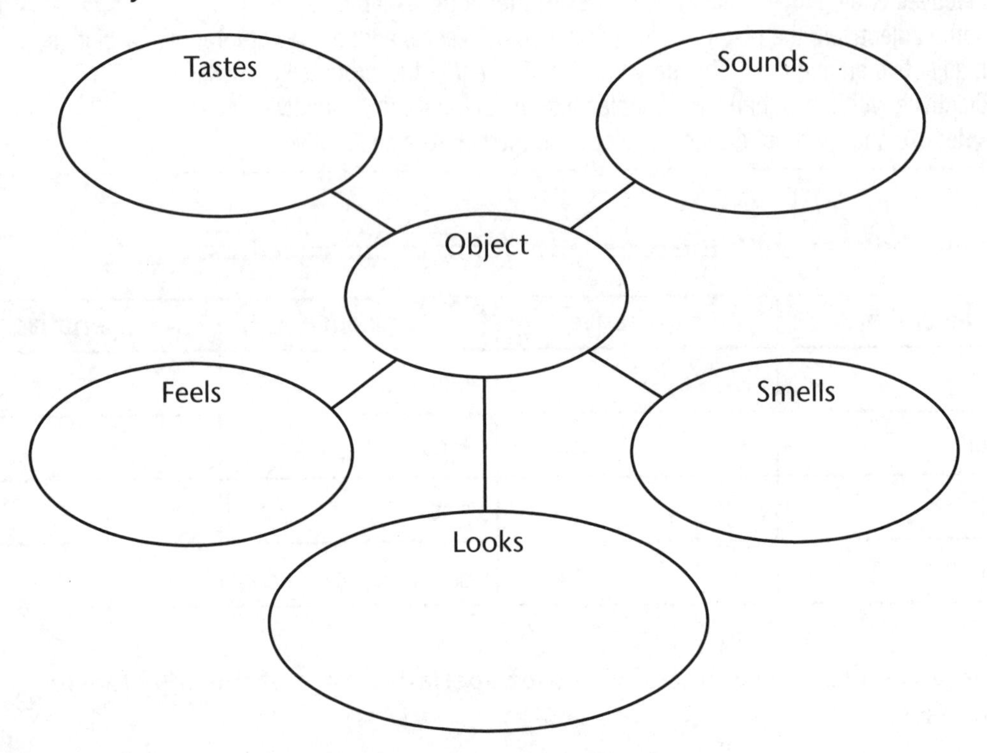

Use the Peer Review Checklist below to obtain feedback from your partner. This feedback will help you edit your final draft.

PEER REVIEW CHECKLIST

- ☐ Does the paragraph describe a fruit or vegetable?
- ☐ Does it describe the object with specificity and detail?
- ☐ Do precise words and details appeal to a reader's senses?
- ☐ Are comparative and superlative adjectives used correctly?
- ☐ Are all words spelled correctly?
- ☐ What changes could be made to improve the paragraph?

Name ______________________________ Date ______________

Can all mysteries be solved?

READING 4: "The Haunted Yacht Club"

VOCABULARY **Literary Words** *Use with textbook page 51.*

REMEMBER The people or animals in a story are called **characters**. Like real people, they have **character traits**, or qualities, that form their personalities. You learn about characters and their traits through what they say and do, and what happens to them in the story. **Plot** is what happens in a story. A plot has a beginning, middle, and end.

Decide if each phrase shows a character, a character trait, or part of a plot. Place a check mark in the correct column.

Phrase	Character	Character Trait	Part of a Plot
knows what he wants		✔	
1. always looks at the bright side of things			
2. the oldest child, Paul			
3. they went to their grandfather's ranch			

Read the paragraph. Then answer the questions that follow.

Alex started packing two weeks before the camping trip. First, he asked his brother Jake if he could borrow his backpack. Jake's backpack was better for hiking than Alex's backpack. He made a list of what he needed. As he found each item, he put a check mark beside it on the list. He had everything. This was his first time camping, and he knew it was going to be perfect. But he heard there was going to be a storm.

4. Who are the characters in the story?

____

5. What character traits does Alex have?

____

6. What do you think will happen in the plot?

____

VOCABULARY Academic Words *Use with textbook page 52.*

Read the paragraph below. Pay attention to the underlined academic words.

Gravity is the force that makes things fall. It's the reason a pen falls down from a table. Isaac Newton was the first individual to identify the force of gravity. He listed several rules of gravity in 1687. He said that gravity didn't just occur on Earth, but also in space. His theory changed the way scientists saw the physical world.

Write the academic words from the paragraph above next to their correct definitions.

Example: ___occur___: happen

1. ________________: an explanation that may or may not be true
2. ________________: relating to the body or to other things you can see, touch, smell, feel, or taste
3. ________________: recognize and name someone or something
4. ________________: a person, not a group

Use the academic words from the paragraph above to complete the sentences.

5. He wanted to be treated like an ________________, not like one of the group.
6. I have a ________________ about whether ghosts are real.
7. American football is a very ________________ game.

Complete the sentences with your own ideas.

Example: One famous theory is ___the theory of gravity___.

8. I can identify ________________________.
9. Here is what I hope will occur this weekend: ________________________.
10. My favorite physical activity is ________________________.

Name ________________________ Date ____________

WORD STUDY **Prefixes *un-, dis-*** *Use with textbook page 53.*

REMEMBER A prefix is a word part added to the beginning of a word that changes the word's meaning. Some prefixes have more than one meaning. For example, the prefix *un-* means "not" or "the opposite of." The prefix *dis-* means "not," "outside of," or "the opposite of." Knowing the meanings of prefixes can help you figure out the meanings of many words you read and hear.

Look at the chart below. Add the prefixes *un-* or *dis-* to each base word to create a new word. Write the new word in the chart. Then write the meaning of the new word.

Prefix	Word	New Word	Definition
un-	wrap	*unwrap*	*"not wrapped"*
1. un-	clear		
2. un-	qualified		
3. dis-	satisfied		
4. dis-	pleased		
5. dis-	content		

Create a new word by adding the prefix *un-* or *dis-* to each word below. Check a dictionary if necessary. Then write the definition next to the new word.

Example: pleasant *unpleasant "not pleasant"*

6. honest ____________

7. organized ____________

8. finished ____________

9. necessary ____________

10. afraid ____________

READING STRATEGY **PREDICT** *Use with textbook page 53.*

REMEMBER You can look for clues in a story that help you predict what will happen next.

Read the paragraphs and answer the questions that follow.

If he could just strike out one more player, Christopher's team would win the game. He held the softball in his hand as the next batter stepped up. The batter looked at Christopher and then up and over his head. Christopher turned to see what he was looking at. The big gray cloud was just about to cover the sun. If it started to rain, the game would be postponed. Christopher didn't want that to happen.

He threw a pitch. The batter swung and hit a foul ball. One strike. Just two more, thought Christopher. The whole field was dark now because of the cloud. He threw the ball. Just one more strike, thought Christopher. But in the distance, he heard a rumble of thunder.

1. What is happening at the beginning of this story?

____

2. What is Christopher trying to do?

____

3. What may prevent Christopher from doing what he wants?

____

4. Make a prediction about what will happen next.

____

5. How can the skill of making a prediction help you to become a better reader?

____

____

Name ______________________________ Date ______________

COMPREHENSION

Use with textbook pages 58–59.

Choose the best answer for each item. Circle the letter of the correct answer.

1. Madison wanted to go on vacation with ______.

   a. the whole family **b.** her father and stepmother **c.** only her father

2. Martha hoped that the vacation would make everyone ______.

   a. happy **b.** busy **c.** tired

3. Madison was ______, but she wanted to show the boys that she was brave.

   a. sad **b.** afraid **c.** young

4. Martha said that ghosts like to ______.

   a. eat cookies **b.** talk to people **c.** do funny things

5. Martha was happy at the end of the story because the children ______.

   a. learned about ghosts **b.** found her and Bob **c.** got along

RESPONSE TO LITERATURE

Use with textbook page 59.

Think of another mystery or adventure story you know. How would Madison, Jimmie, and Danny act in this story? Write a paragraph describing it.

____

____

____

____

____

GRAMMAR **Single-Word Prepositions of Location**

Use with textbook page 60.

REMEMBER Many single word prepositions can be used to show a location or place. A preposition is followed by a noun or noun phrase called a prepositional phrase. It answers the question *Where*? A prepositional phrase of location usually appears at the end of a sentence or clause.

Circle True or False.

1. Prepositions of location tell you where something is. True False
2. Prepositions are followed by a verb. True False
3. Prepositions can be followed by a phrase. True False
4. Propositions often come at the end of a sentence. True False

REMEMBER Use *in* with a city, state, country, or closed area; use *on* with a surface; use *at* with a specific place.

Circle the correct preposition.

1. Point Isabel is (in / on / at) the United States.
2. Madison was crying (in / on / at) her bedroom.
3. They were going to stay (in / on / at) the Haunted Yacht Club.
4. Many large yachts were bobbing (in / on / at) the water.
5. Martha was standing (in / on / at) the patio.
6. Madison held the cookies tightly (in / on / at) her hand.

Name ______________________________ Date ______________

Multi-Word Prepositions of Location *Use with textbook page 61.*

REMEMBER A multi-word preposition is made up of more than one word, but it has a single meaning. It is followed by a noun or a noun phrase.

Circle the multi-word prepositions of location.

1. We stood in front of the boat.
2. She saw a man next to the gangplank.
3. She crouched in between the two other children.
4. A shadow fell on top of the crate.
5. He took the cookies out of her hand.

Complete the sentences with the correct preposition from the box.

to	of	in	front	behind	on

6. Madison crouched down next ______________ Danny and Jimmie.
7. The cookies fell ______________ top of the crate.
8. They were hiding ______________ between two crates.
9. They looked out from ______________ the crates.
10. The ghost was standing there in ______________ of them.

Write sentences using these words.

11. the cat / next / the fire / sat / to

____

12. in / girl / the box / between / hid / the wall / and

____

WRITING Write a Description of a Character

Use with textbook pages 62–63.

Complete your own T-chart for a paragraph describing someone you know.

Physical traits	Character traits

Use the Peer Review Checklist below to obtain feedback from your partner. This feedback will help you edit your final draft.

PEER REVIEW CHECKLIST

- ☐ Does the paragraph describe someone the writer knows?
- ☐ Does it describe both physical traits and character traits?
- ☐ Do precise words and details create a vivid image of the person?
- ☐ Is the writing voice clear and lively?
- ☐ Are prepositions of location used correctly?
- ☐ What changes could be made to improve the paragraph?

Name ________________________________ Date ______________

WRITING WORKSHOP *Use with textbook page 68.*

Organize your ideas in the graphic organizer below.

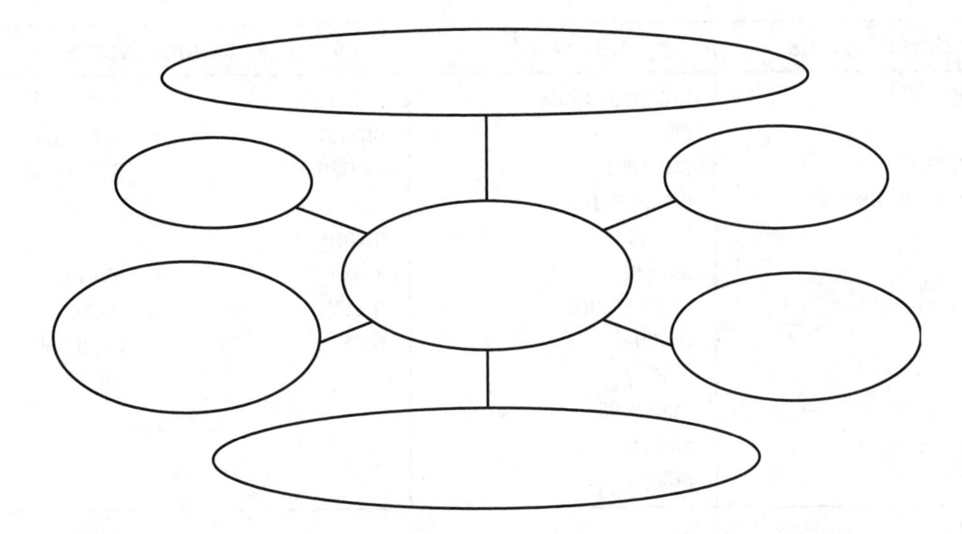

Use the Peer Review Checklist below to obtain feedback from your partner. This feedback will help you edit your final draft.

PEER REVIEW CHECKLIST

- ☐ Does the essay describe an amazing scene?
- ☐ Does it include precise words and vivid sensory details?
- ☐ Is the writing lively and engaging?
- ☐ Are verbs, tenses, and pronoun/antecedents used correctly?
- ☐ Are comparison structures used correctly?
- ☐ What changes could be made to improve the essay?

LEARNING LOG *Use after completing page 72.*

Underline the vocabulary items you know and can use well. Review and practice any you haven't underlined. Underline them when you know them well.

Literary Words	Key Words	Academic Words	
idioms	archaeologist	accurate	constant
puns	clues	create	illustrate
characters	creature	evidence	sequence
character traits	disappeared	survive	unique
plot	fantasy	aware	identify
	sacred	intelligent	individual
	architecture	motive	occur
	gradual	pursue	physical
	infinity		theory
	numerals		
	spirals		
	steep		

Put a check by the skills you can perform well. Review and practice any you haven't checked off. Check them off when you can perform them well.

Skills	I can . . .
Word Study	☐ spell words with the same sound but different spellings. ☐ recognize and use compound nouns. ☐ spell words with *ai, ay, ee,* and *oa.* ☐ recognize and use the prefixes *un-, dis-*.
Reading Strategies	☐ preview. ☐ draw conclusions. ☐ use visuals. ☐ predict.
Grammar	☐ distinguish parts of speech and parts of the sentence. ☐ use possessive nouns, adjectives, and pronouns and indefinite pronouns. ☐ use comparison structures. ☐ use prepositions of location.
Writing	☐ describe a place. ☐ describe an event. ☐ describe an object. ☐ describe a character. ☐ write a descriptive essay.

TEST 1

DIRECTIONS
Read this selection. Then answer the questions that follow it.

Vacation Planning

Tania and Jill hike every weekend. They have visited many places in New Jersey. This weekend they are planning a trip to Ocean Grove. They want to spend some time at the beach.

City of Origin	Miles to Ocean Grove	Approximate Driving Time
Newark	50	1 hour, 8 minutes
Trenton	46	53 minutes
Edison	37	49 minutes
Camden	77	1 hour, 30 minutes

1 What best describes what Tania and Jill like to do?
- A Go hiking
- B Go to the beach
- C Visit cities
- D Visit Ocean Grove

2 If Tania and Jill live in Camden, how long will it take them to get to Ocean Grove?
- F 1 hour
- G 1 hour, 30 minutes
- H 77 minutes
- J 49 minutes

3 What does driving time mean?
- A The time on the clock
- B The speed you are driving
- C How far away something is
- D How long it takes to get somewhere

TEST 2

DIRECTIONS
Read this selection. Then answer the questions that follow it.

Eshu's Hat

1 One day, Eshu played a trick on two farmers. He put on a hat that was red on one side and blue on the other. Then he walked down the main road of the village. The farmers looked up from their work as Eshu passed by. One farmer saw Eshu wearing a red hat, and the other saw him wearing a blue hat. After Eshu had passed the village, he stopped and turned the hat around on his head, then walked back down the road in the opposite direction.

2 After Eshu had passed, one farmer said to the other, "What a fashionable red hat Eshu is wearing!" The other farmer said, "It is stylish, but you are certainly wrong. He was wearing a blue hat!"

3 The farmers began arguing over the color of Eshu's hat. They argued so loudly that the other villagers heard them and joined in. Half of the villagers sided with one farmer. The other half sided with the other farmer.

4 Suddenly Eshu appeared. He told the villagers, "I can solve the mystery. All of you are right, and all of you are wrong!" Then he showed them his hat. "You are arguing because you looked at my hat from only one side!"

1 Paragraph 1 is mostly about —

A the farmers' crops
B the farmers' argument
C Eshu's trick
D the color of Eshu's shoes

2 The reader can conclude that —

F Eshu likes to play tricks on people
G the farmers like to argue
H the villagers like Eshu
J Eshu likes to solve mysteries

3 Which words from paragraph 3 best help the reader understand what *fashionable* means?

A wearing
B certainly
C passed
D stylish

4 According to the selection, the villagers are arguing because —

F they like one farmer more than the other
G they are not happy about Eshu's trick
H they don't know that the hat has two different colors
J they all think the hat is red

Name ______________________ Date __________

TEST 3

DIRECTIONS
Read the selection. Then answer the questions that follow it.

Bigfoot

Bigfoot Stories

1 One night in 1924, Albert Ostman was camping in a forest near Vancouver, Canada. Asleep deep in the woods, he suddenly awoke when something lifted his sleeping bag off the ground. Ostman screamed. Whatever had lifted him quickly put him down. Ostman crawled out of his sleeping bag and saw a large, hairy creature. According to Ostman, the creature looked back at him and then ran into the forest. Ostman claimed he had seen the legendary Bigfoot. There are many other stories about Bigfoot. Before the Europeans arrived in America, Native Americans told stories of an ape-like creature. Today, there are thousands of reported sightings of this creature.

How to Recognize a Bigfoot

2 People who have reported seeing a bigfoot claim the creatures look like giant apes. They also say that a bigfoot has hair all over its body, has a strange smell, makes strange sounds, and has very big feet.

Proof

3 Is there proof that Bigfoot exists? Some people think so. Many people claim to have seen the footprints of Bigfoot, which are said to be up to twenty inches long. Other people claim to have photographs. No one had photographed a Bigfoot until Robert Patterson made a film in 1967. Patterson said he was in a forest in northern California when he saw a bigfoot. Patterson said he was hiking when he saw a bigfoot walking near a riverbank. Patterson grabbed his movie camera and filmed the creature as it hurried away into the forest.

Real or Fake

4 Some people say Patterson's movie is a fake. They say that Bigfoot is really a man in an ape costume. However, some experts have studied the film closely. They believe it is Bigfoot because he moves like a real ape. These experts say that a man in a costume could not move so naturally.

5 Since Patterson made his film, many other people have said they've seen a bigfoot or found his footprints in the ground. Some people claim to have taken pictures of a bigfoot. Are these stories real or fake? The mystery may never be solved.

1 Look at the chart below.

How can you recognize a bigfoot?

He looks like an ape.		He has hair all over his body.	He has very big feet.

Which of these belongs in the empty box?

A He walks like a human.
B He snorts like a pig.
C He runs quickly.
D He has a strange smell.

2 The selection is best described as —

F informative
G funny
H sad
J entertaining

3 The author organizes this selection by —

A telling about four different sightings of Bigfoot
B describing a sighting, Bigfoot's appearance, proof, and expert opinions
C explaining the history and stories about Bigfoot throughout time
D listing examples of proof that Bigfoot is real

4 Which sentence from the selection best supports the idea that the story of Bigfoot has been passed down for hundreds of years?

F *Asleep deep in the woods, he suddenly awoke when something lifted his sleeping bag off the ground.*
G *Before the Europeans arrived in America, Native Americans told stories of an ape-like creature.*
H *No one had photographed a bigfoot until Robert Patterson made a film in 1967.*
J *Today, there are thousands of reported sightings of this creature.*

Name ______________________________ Date ______________

Visual Literacy: Smithsonian American Art Museum *Use with textbook pages 74–75*

LEARNING TO LOOK

Look at *Preamble* by Mike Wilkins on page 74. Describe six things you see in this artwork. State facts, not opinions.

Example: *Many of the license plates are blue.*

1. ______________________________

2. ______________________________

3. ______________________________

4. ______________________________

5. ______________________________

6. ______________________________

INTERPRETATION

Look at *Five* by Robert Indiana on page 75. Imagine that you are driving down the highway and see *Five* on the side of the road. What do you see? Write where you think the artwork is telling you to go.

Example: *It's a sign for an old general store and it's telling me it's just five miles ahead.*

____

____

____

____

____

____

5W&H

Look at *Preamble* by Mike Wilkins on page 74. Imagine you could interview the artist about this artwork. What would you want to know? Use *Who, Where, When, What, Why,* and *How* to frame your questions.

Example: How *did you get the idea for this artwork?*

1. **Who** ______________________________

____

2. **Where** ______________________________

____

3. **When** ______________________________

____

4. **What** ______________________________

____

5. **Why** ______________________________

____

6. **How** ______________________________

____

Name ______________________________ Date ______________

How does growing up change us?

READING 1: "Ancient Kids"

VOCABULARY **Key Words** *Use with textbook page 79.*

Write each word in the box next to its definition.

ancient	ceremony	citizen	education	rights	rituals

Example: ___rights___: things you are allowed to do, according to law or moral ideas

1. ______________: process of learning in a school or other program of study
2. ______________: ceremonies that are always done the same way
3. ______________: someone who lives in a particular town, state, or country
4. ______________: formal event that happens in public on special occasions
5. ______________: happening or existing very far back in history

Use the words in the box at the top of the page to complete the sentences.

6. My grandfather is a ______________ of the United States of America.
7. I believe that every child should go to school and get a good ______________.
8. The mask the archaeologist found in the old palace was ______________.
9. The priest performed all of the ______________ the same way every week.
10. A family member's wedding ______________ is a very important tradition in my family.

VOCABULARY **Academic Words** *Use with textbook page 80.*

Read the paragraph below. Pay attention to the underlined academic words.

> The arts and literature of the classical societies of Greece and Rome still have an impact on our own cultural life today. Each feature of ancient art can be seen in the paintings and sculptures of our own day and time. The writings of Greek philosophers, such as Plato and Socrates, still influence modern philosophy. And modern plays have many elements from classical theater.

Write the academic words from the paragraph above next to their correct definitions.

Example: *philosophy*: the study of what it means to exist, what good and evil are, what knowledge is, or how people should live

1. ______________: quality, element, or characteristic of something that seems important, interesting, or typical

2. ______________: relating to a particular society and its way of life

3. ______________: belonging to the culture of ancient Greece or ancient Rome

Use the academic words from the paragraph above to complete the sentences.

4. An interesting ______________ of this flower is its unusual petals.

5. I want to study the ______________ writers of the Roman period in my English class.

6. Studying ______________ made her wonder about the meaning of life.

7. There are many ______________ differences between the two countries.

Complete the sentences with your own ideas.

Example: I think that life in classical Greece was *very exciting*.

8. One feature I have that is unusual is ______________.

9. I think that attending cultural activities and sporting events is ______________ ______________.

10. The study of philosophy is ______________.

Name ______________________________ Date ______________

WORD STUDY **Spelling Words with Long Vowel Sound /ē/**

Use with textbook page 81.

REMEMBER The long /ē/ sound can be spelled several different ways. These include *e* as in *she*, *ee* as in *street*, *ea* as in *wheat*, *ie* as in *yield*, *y* as in *lady*, and *ey* as in *donkey*. Knowing these patterns helps you spell and say the words correctly.

Read the words in the box. Then write each word in the correct column in the chart.

~~even~~	each	irony	achieve	monkey	thief
season	shady	evil	beet	attorney	weekend

Long e spelled *e*	Long e spelled *ee*	Long e spelled *ea*
even		
Long e spelled *ie*	**Long e spelled *y***	**Long e spelled *ey***

Write the letter-sound pattern in each word.

Example: we *long /e/ spelled e*

1. cheap ______________
2. chief ______________
3. botany ______________
4. barley ______________
5. speed ______________
6. agony ______________
7. sweet ______________
8. siege ______________
9. speak ______________

READING STRATEGY COMPARE AND CONTRAST

Use with textbook page 81.

REMEMBER Comparing and contrasting things in a selection help you recall what you read. When you compare, you show how things, ideas, facts, persons, events, and stories are the same. When you contrast, you show how things, ideas, facts, persons, events, and stories are different.

Read each paragraph and answer the questions that follow.

Connor missed his friends and his room at home in the city. He wanted to play soccer down at the park and go for ice cream afterwards. He even missed the school and the cars buzzing by the playground all afternoon.

After a while, however, he began to like it at his grandfather's house. The quiet was so different from home. And he loved the bay. He liked fishing and throwing stones into the water. He even liked hearing about his grandfather's time in the military.

1. **How are the city and the bay different?**

____

2. **How does Connor feel about the different places he has lived?**

____

Sarah was puzzled. She looked at the two dogs. They were so different. One was small and fluffy and jumped around a lot. The other was bigger, moved less, and gave Sarah goofy looks.

The man who ran the shelter said, "They are both two years old and ready for adoption. It really depends on what you're looking for."

Sarah thought she was looking for a small dog. However, there was something about the big eyes of the bigger dog she really liked. This was going to be a tough decision.

3. **In what ways are the dogs alike?**

____

4. **In what ways are the dogs different?**

____

5. **How does comparing and contrasting help you to understand a story?**

____

Name ______________________________ Date ____________

COMPREHENSION

Use with textbook page 88.

Choose the best answer for each item. Circle the letter of the correct answer.

1. In ancient Greece, boys went to school and ______.

   a. girls went to school, too
   b. girls stayed at home and helped their mothers
   c. girls worked outside of the home

2. What did boys in ancient Greece learn about at school?

   a. the arts, war, and how to be a good citizen
   b. science, technology, and computers
   c. English, Spanish, and Chinese

3. Who was the "head of the family" in ancient Rome?

   a. the eldest son in the family
   b. the mother
   c. the oldest male in the family

4. Which jobs were women in ancient Rome not allowed to have?

   a. lawyer, teacher, and government jobs
   b. mother and homemaker
   c. farmer and maker of crafts

5. Did poor children go to school in ancient Rome?

   a. Yes, they went to school.
   b. No, they studied at home with their parents.
   c. They did not go to school or study anywhere.

EXTENSION

Use with textbook page 89.

In the column on the left, list five things that you think were fun about living in one of the ancient cultures you read about. In the column on the right, list five things that you think were difficult about living in one of the ancient cultures.

Fun Times	Difficult Times
learning how to sail boats	*girls couldn't continue in school*

GRAMMAR Showing Contrast: Coordinating Conjunctions

Use with textbook page 90.

REMEMBER The coordinating conjunctions *but* and *yet* contrast two ideas. The conjunction usually begins the second clause and is preceded by a comma. The second clause shows the unexpected result.
Example: My friend loves reading books, but I prefer watching movies.

Circle the best way to complete each sentence.

1. In ancient Greece, boys went to school, but ______.

   a. girls had to stay home **b.** girls learned to play musical instruments

2. In ancient Rome, boys and girls could go to school, yet ______.

   a. poor families could not afford school **b.** children went to school at age seven

3. Mayan boys and girls played with toys that had wheels, but ______.

   a. the Maya did not use wheels for transportation **b.** the Maya used animals in their art

Choose an ending from the boxes to make a sentence with the best contrast.

but they did have a system of writing.	yet they also offer great enjoyment.	but the Romans used bricks.	yet they also grew cotton and beans.	but the Greeks built things of great beauty.

4. The Romans built useful things, ______________________________

5. The Greeks used marble in their buildings, ______________________________

6. The Maya people's main crop was corn, ______________________________

Name ______________________________ Date ______________

Showing Contrast: Conjunctive Adverbs *Use with textbook page 91.*

REMEMBER A conjunctive adverb is used with two complete sentences. The conjunctive adverb begins the second sentence and is followed by a comma. The second sentence shows an unexpected result. Some examples are *however, nevertheless,* and *nonetheless.*
Example: My family wants to go skiing. However, it did not snow very much this month.

Match the sentences below. Then rewrite them using conjunctive adverbs.

_______ Animals were important to the Maya people in everyday life and religion.

_______ In ancient Greece, children did not have school books.

_______ In ancient Rome, women were not allowed to hold jobs in government.

_______ They learned poetry and stories from history.

_______ They were allowed to own land.

_______ They sometimes ate dogs and buried them with their owners.

1. ______________________________

2. ______________________________

3. ______________________________

Write a new sentence that will contrast with each sentence below. Use the conjunctive adverb in parenthesis.

4. (However) Both cats and dogs make good pets. ______________________________

____

5. (Nevertheless) Sometimes rainy days are boring. ______________________________

____

6. (Nonetheless) Both gold and silver are metals. ______________________________

____

WRITING Write a Friendly Letter *Use with textbook pages 92–93.*

Complete your own "parts of a letter" organizer for a friendly letter to an older family member.

(Date)

(Greeting)

(Body)

(Closing)
(Signature)

Use the Peer Review Checklist below to obtain feedback from your partner. This feedback will help you edit your final draft.

PEER REVIEW CHECKLIST

- ☐ Is the letter addressed to an older family member?
- ☐ Does it include all five parts of a friendly letter?
- ☐ Does it tell a story about an event in the writer's life?
- ☐ Does it tell what happened in time order?
- ☐ Are coordinating conjunctions used correctly?
- ☐ What changes could be made to improve the letter?

Name ______________________________ Date ____________

How does growing up change us?

READING 2: From *Becoming Naomi León*

VOCABULARY **Literary Words** *Use with textbook page 95.*

REMEMBER **Dialogue** is the exact words spoken by two or more characters. Writers use dialogue to show what the characters in a story are like.
Example: "I am too tired to play another game," said Rosa.
The **setting** is the time and place where a story occurs. Identifying the setting will help you understand what is happening in the story.
Example: The sun rose so hot over the Arizona desert that Lucia awoke at first light.

Read each sentence. Write *setting* if it describes a setting. Write *dialogue* if it gives words spoken by characters.

Setting or Dialogue	Sentence
setting	When I was a young man, I lived in New York City. It was 1920, the year I turned fifteen.
1.	Julie pressed her face to the airplane window. "Oh Mom, I'm so excited!" she said. "In another hour we'll be in France!"
2.	Nate woke up and immediately remembered that it was New Year's Day. "Welcome to 2008," he said to himself.
3.	Mandy had lived in the same small town in Ohio her whole life. She loved it there. She had known all her friends since kindergarten.
4.	I'd never really wanted to visit my aunt in Mexico, but now that I was spending the summer here, I was very excited.
5.	It was the year 1988. I'd just started the sixth grade at Bedford Junior High in Marion, Kentucky.

On the lines below write a brief dialogue. You can use made-up characters or people you know. Be sure to give a setting.

____

____

____

____

VOCABULARY Academic Words *Use with textbook page 96.*

Read the paragraph. Pay attention to the underlined academic words.

> Sometimes two people have a conflict they can't solve. In this case, it's often wise to seek a counselor. The counselor can assist by guiding them through the process of conflict resolution. The counselor can also help them strengthen the bond they feel with each other.

Write the letter of the correct definition next to each word.

Example: ___c___ assist

_____ **1.** conflict

_____ **2.** bond

_____ **3.** process

a. a series of actions that someone does in order to achieve a particular result

b. disagreement

c. help someone do something

d. a feeling or interest that unites two or more people or groups

Use the academic words from the exercise above to complete the sentences.

4. Mary had a ____________________ with her brother about washing the dishes.

5. I enjoy the ____________________ of developing photographs.

6. Because they both liked soccer, the boys developed a strong ____________________.

7. Because he can cook so well, my father will ____________________ me with making dinner.

Complete the sentences with your own ideas.

Example: I like to assist my friends with *their math homework*.

8. There was a conflict among my friends about ______________________________.

9. I am interested in the process of ______________________________.

10. The family member I have the closest bond with is ______________________________

because ______________________________.

Name ______________________________ Date ______________

WORD STUDY Suffixes *-ness, -tion,* and *-ation*

Use with textbook page 97.

REMEMBER A *suffix* is a letter or letters added to the end of a word to make a new word. Suffixes change the word's part of speech and meaning. Sometimes the word's spelling changes when a suffix is added, as in *note* + *ation* = *notation.*

Look at the chart. Add the suffix *-ness, -tion,* or *-ation* as directed to create a new word. Write the new word on the chart. Then write the meaning.

Word	Suffix	New Word	Definition
Example: sad	-ness	*sadness*	*unhappiness*
1. willing	-ness		
2. digest	-tion		
3. motivate	-tion		
4. reserve	-ation		
5. calculate	-ation		

Create a new word by adding the suffix *-ness, -tion,* or *-ation* to each word. Use a dictionary if needed. Then write the definition next to the new word.

Example: float *+ ation = flotation a device that helps something float*

6. eager ______________________________

7. investigate ______________________________

8. inspire ______________________________

9. create ______________________________

10. stipulate ______________________________

READING STRATEGY **VISUALIZE** *Use with textbook page 97.*

REMEMBER When you visualize something you've read, you make a picture of it in your mind. When you read, notice descriptive words and the images the writer has created.

Read the paragraph and answer the questions that follow.

Langston thought it was the most awesome thing he'd ever seen. The whale was blue-gray and glistening just below the surface of the water. It was so large and so close that from where he was standing, he couldn't see the head or the tail, just the massive body. It was gliding by in the water, just twenty feet from his boat. Slowly the whale started to descend into the water, the shimmering skin becoming just a dark patch. Moments later, he saw a spurt of water about 20 yards from the ship—water from the whale's blowhole. It seemed to Langston that the whale was saying goodbye.

1. **What is the story about?**

____

2. **What is the strongest image in the passage?**

____

3. **What words in the passage help you to make a mental picture of the whale?**

____

4. **How can the skill of visualizing help you to understand a text more clearly?**

____

5. **Draw a picture of the scene described in the passage. Be sure to include details from the passage in your drawing.**

Name ______________________________ Date ______________

COMPREHENSION

Use with textbook pages 104–105.

Choose the best answer for each item. Circle the letter of the correct answer.

1. Naomi and her father bonded through ______.

   a. carving **b.** playing games together **c.** travelling

2. Naomi's father taught her ______.

   a. how to sell his carvings **b.** how to cook special Mexican dishes **c.** how to find the magic in the figurines

3. Naomi, her brother, and her grandmother leave Mexico ______.

   a. with her father **b.** to go back to California to settle the custody problem **c.** and move to Arizona

4. Naomi's father told her not to be sad because ______.

   a. they found each other and everything was fine **b.** he made her a special gift to remember him by **c.** they would live in Mexico

5. It is hard for Naomi to leave Mexico because ______.

   a. she hates the weather in California **b.** she is worried about her future **c.** she doesn't want to live with her grandmother

RESPONSE TO LITERATURE

Use with textbook page 105.

Write a few sentences explaining what you think Naomi meant by the statement ***My pen seemed too heavy to lift.***

____

____

____

____

____

GRAMMAR **Count and Non-count Nouns** *Use with textbook page 106.*

REMEMBER A singular count noun may be preceded by *a*, *an*, or *the*. A plural count noun usually ends in *-s* or *-es* and may be preceded by *the*. A non-count noun will not be preceded by *a* or *an*. It has no plural, so it does not end in *-s* or *-es*. A non-count noun may also be preceded by *the*.

Write the words in the box in the correct place in the chart.

rain	dog	tree	biology	grammar	bird	house	soccer	snow	bicycle

Non-count Nouns	Count Nouns

Add *a* or *an* if it is needed.

1. Do you like to study ________________ math?
2. Is this ________________ lemon tree?
3. Do you have ________________ snow in your country?
4. Can I have ________________ apple?
5. The most important thing is ________________ love.
6. This carving is made from ________________ wood.

Write sentences using each of the words below.

7. (rain) ________________________________
8. (English) ________________________________
9. (dictionary) ________________________________
10. (computer) ________________________________

Name ________________________ Date ____________

Quantifiers *Use with textbook page 107.*

REMEMBER Some quantifiers are used with count nouns, some are used with non-count nouns, and some are used with both.

Which quantifiers are used with count nouns? Which are used with non-count nouns? Which are used with both?

several	many	much	a great deal of	a lot of	some	a little	each	every	any

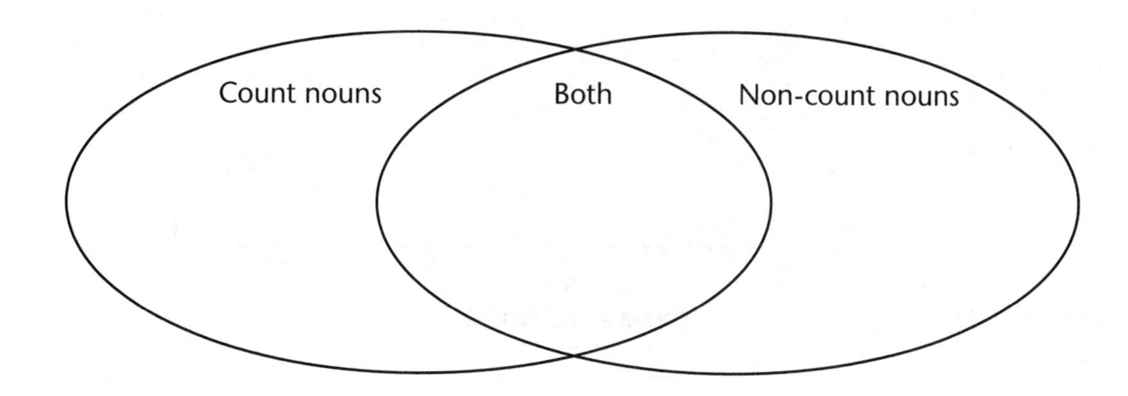

Circle the correct answer.

1. We spent ______ vacation by the ocean. **a.** every **b.** a few
2. There isn't ______ time to talk. **a.** much **b.** many
3. I could see ______ purple flowers. **a.** a lot of **b.** a great deal of
4. He made ______ carvings from wood. **a.** a few **b.** a little
5. You don't need ______ money. **a.** any **b.** many
6. Do you have ______ bags? **a.** many **b.** a great deal of

Make a list of three things you can see in your classroom. Use quantifiers to describe how much or how many there is / are of each thing.

Example: windows *There are a lot of windows*.

7. ____________ ________________________

8. ____________ ________________________

9. ____________ ________________________

WRITING Write about a Character and Setting

Use with textbook pages 108–109.

Complete your own chart for a paragraph about a made-up character in a realistic setting.

Character (Who)
Setting (Where and When)

Use the Peer Review Checklist below to obtain feedback from your partner. This feedback will help you edit your final draft.

PEER REVIEW CHECKLIST

- ☐ Does the writer create an interesting character?
- ☐ Does the writer tell how the character looks, acts, and thinks?
- ☐ Are precise words used to describe a believable setting?
- ☐ Does the writer narrate events with specificity and detail?
- ☐ Are grammar and usage correct, including subject-verb agreement?
- ☐ What changes could be made to improve the story?

Name ______________________________ Date ______________

How does growing up change us?

READING 3: "Amazing Growth Facts" / "The Old Grandfather and His Little Grandson"

VOCABULARY **Key Words** *Use with textbook page 111.*

Write each word in the box next to its definition.

average	conversion	height	length	rate	weight

Example: ___average___: having qualities that are typical of most people or things

1. ____________________: when you change something from one form, system, or purpose to another
2. ____________________: the measurement of something from one end to another
3. ____________________: the number of times something happens over a period of time
4. ____________________: how heavy someone or something is
5. ____________________: how tall someone or something is

Use the words in the box at the top of the page to complete the sentences.

6. I use a ____________________ chart to change miles to kilometers.
7. When I went to the doctor, she measured my ____________________ with a tape measure.
8. When I measured the ____________________ of the hallway, I discovered that it was longer than I had expected.
9. I am tall for my age; my mom says my height is above ____________________.
10. My hair grows at a very fast ____________________.

VOCABULARY **Academic Words** *Use with textbook page 112.*

Read the paragraph below. Pay attention to the underlined academic words.

It's important to eat plenty of foods from the fruit and vegetable <u>category</u> of the food chart. One major <u>benefit</u> of eating fruits and vegetables is all the vitamins they give you. For example, broccoli contains an <u>enormous</u> amount of vitamin C. Just one serving of broccoli contains 220 <u>percent</u> of the recommended daily allowance of vitamin C.

Write the letter of the correct definition next to each word.

Example: __c__ benefit

_____ **1.** category

_____ **2.** percent

_____ **3.** enormous

a. equal to a particular amount in every hundred

b. extremely large in size or amount

c. something that gives you an advantage, that helps you, or that has a good effect

d. group of people or things that have related characteristics

Use the academic words from the exercise above to complete the sentences.

4. The treasurer had a _______________ for each type of expense.

5. On her way to school, Ann Marie saw an _______________ bird that looked like a hawk.

6. Extra help with my science project will be a huge _______________ to me.

7. I was glad when 60 _______________ of the students supported my brother for class president.

Complete the sentences with your own ideas.

Example: I am in the same age category as *my friend Alicia*.

8. An enormous challenge I have faced is _______________.

9. The benefit of going to school is _______________.

10. I agreed with my friend one hundred percent when he said

_______________.

Name ______________________________ Date ______________

WORD STUDY Spelling Words with Long Vowel Sound /ō/

Use with textbook page 113.

REMEMBER The long /ō/ can be spelled in many ways, including *o* as in *hold*, *o_e* as in *bone*, *oa* as in *oak*, and *ow* as in *blow*. Knowing these four patterns can help you spell many words with the long /ō/ correctly.

Read the words in the box. Then write each word in the correct column in the chart.

~~robot~~	below	goat	cone	pillow	joke
coast	soda	grove	shallow	roast	host

/ō/ spelled *o*	/ō/ spelled *o_e*	/ō/ spelled *oa*	/ō/ spelled *ow*
robot			

Write the spelling of long /ō/ in each word.

Example: toast *_/ō/ spelled oa_*

1. mold ______________

2. zone ______________

3. flown ______________

4. gloat ______________

5. sold ______________

6. grown ______________

7. bow ______________

8. vote ______________

9. role ______________

READING STRATEGY USE VISUALS 2

Use with textbook page 113.

REMEMBER You use visuals in a text to help you understand what is happening. Visuals can be charts, maps, photographs, drawings, or diagrams.

Look at the pictures and text and answer the questions that follow.

Adult Animals and Their Eggs

Egg Size No Indication of Adult Size

The Golden Eagle has an egg the same size as that of the Nile Crocodile. But while the adult Golden Eagle only reaches 88 cm when full grown, the Nile Crocodile will grow to 5 meters!

U.S. Units

It is easier to understand how big the eggs and animals are if we convert their sizes into U.S. units. Take a look at the chart to see how the measurement rates compare.

Conversion Chart

Metric		U.S. Customary Units
1 millimeter	=	0.039 inch
1 centimeter	=	0.39 inch
1 meter	=	3.28 feet
1 gram	=	0.035 ounce
1 kilogram	=	2.2 pounds

1. What do you think the article is about?

___

2. How do the pictures help you to understand the text?

___

3. How does the chart help you to understand the text?

___

4. What is one thing you learned from the information given?

___

5. How do you think the skill of using visuals can help you to understand the text?

___

Name ______________________________ Date ____________

COMPREHENSION *Use with textbook page 118.*

Choose the best answer for each item. Circle the letter of the correct answer.

1. One of the longest living creatures is the ______.

a. eagle **b.** human **c.** clam

2. As children, boys and girls are usually about the same ______.

a. weight, but not height **b.** height, but not weight **c.** height and weight

3. An ant can lift more than one hundred times its ______.

a. rate **b.** weight **c.** height

4. The average human life span is about ______.

a. 70 years **b.** 50 years **c.** 100 years

5. All living things ______ in size.

a. decrease **b.** increase **c.** fall

EXTENSION *Use with textbook page 119.*

The folk tale "The Old Grandfather and His Little Grandson" is a reminder that you should treat people with care and respect. You should treat people the way you wish to be treated. Write a sentence describing how you like to be treated. Write a sentence about how you do not like to be treated.

I like to be treated:

____

____

I do not like to be treated:

____

____

GRAMMAR Simple Past: Regular Verbs *Use with textbook page 120.*

REMEMBER Use the simple past to talk about actions that began and ended in the past. Form the simple past by adding *-d* or *-ed* to the base form.
Example: I walked to the zoo.
If a verb ends in a consonant plus vowel plus consonant, you must double the consonant before adding *-ed*.
Example: I nodded to my sister.
If the verb ends in consonant plus *y*, change *y* to *i* and add *-ed*.
Example: I hurried to school.

Change the verbs in the box to the simple past and write them in the correct place in the chart.

live	drop	try	play	watch	stop	carry	increase	enjoy	rain	like	nod

Add *-d*	Add *-ed*	Change *y* to *i*, add *-ed*	Double consonant, add *-ed*

Circle the correct verb form.

1. We (watch / watched) the soccer game yesterday.
2. She did not (cry / cried) when she lost the game.
3. Did you (finish / finished) your homework?
4. It didn't (rain / rained) last weekend.
5. We (enjoy / enjoyed) the dinner last night.
6. What food did you (like / liked) when you were little?

Name ______________________________ Date ______________

Simple Past: Irregular Verbs *Use with textbook page 121.*

REMEMBER Irregular verbs do not make the simple past by adding *-d* or *-ed*. Every verb is different and you will need to memorize them.

Complete the chart with the simple past of each verb.

Base form	Simple past		Base form	Simple past
give	*gave*		let	
make			eat	
say			take	
be			break	

Complete each sentence with the correct simple past form of the verbs in the box.

break	eat	have	let	make	say

1. The grandfather ______________ no teeth.
2. He ______________ his meals in the corner.
3. "Did you ______________ that bowl?" she said.
4. The old man didn't ______________ anything.
5. The boy ______________ a bowl out of wood.
6. They ______________ the old man eat with them.

Use the verbs below to write sentences about what you did (or didn't do) last weekend. Cross out the words when you use them. Try to cross out a line of verbs.

buy	read	find
eat	see	do
play	watch	clean

7. ______________________________
8. ______________________________
9. ______________________________

WRITING Write a Story from a Different Point of View

Use with textbook pages 122–123.

Complete your own T-chart contrasting the perspectives of the original narrator from a familiar story and another character's point of view.

Familiar Point of View	New Point of View

Use the Peer Review Checklist below to obtain feedback from your partner. This feedback will help you edit your final draft.

PEER REVIEW CHECKLIST

- ☐ Does the writer retell a familiar story?
- ☐ Is the story retold from a new point of view?
- ☐ Does the writing voice fit the story's new narrator?
- ☐ Are first-person pronouns used correctly?
- ☐ Is the simple past tense used correctly?
- ☐ What changes could be made to improve the story?

Name ______________________ Date ______________

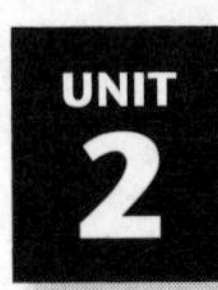

How does growing up change us?

READING 4: "Thirty Dollars"

VOCABULARY **Literary Words** *Use with textbook page 125.*

REMEMBER **Point of view** is the position from which a story is told. Some stories are told from the first-person point of view.
Example: I couldn't wait to get home.
Other stories are told from the third-person point of view.
Example: Melissa couldn't wait to get home.
The **narrator** is the person telling the story. The narrator can be a character in the story or someone telling it from the outside.

Read the passage below. Answer the questions that follow.

Strange things happened the summer my little brother was nine. It was the craziest summer of our lives. It was also the most fun. My little brother's name is Tom. I'm David, and I'm going to tell you one unbelievable story.

1. What point of view is used in the story?

   ____

2. Who is the narrator?

   ____

3. What words in the paragraph would be different if it were told from another point of view?

   ____

Think of an idea for a story. What is it about? Describe the plot in the box on the left. Then write a brief description of the point of view and narrator in the box on the right.

4.	5.

VOCABULARY Academic Words *Use with textbook page 126.*

Read the paragraph. Pay attention to the underlined academic words.

I just read a book about therapy dogs, the dogs that visit patients in hospitals. A therapy dog can affect a patient's mood, making the patient feel happier and more hopeful. In fact, the dog's visit can have a positive effect on the patient's health. The author of the book was able to document a lot of interesting information, including his belief that not all dogs can be therapy dogs. From his perspective, a dog must have a calm, friendly, and outgoing personality to be a good therapy dog.

Write the letter of the correct definition next to each word.

Example: ___b___ affect

_____ **1.** document

_____ **2.** effect

_____ **3.** perspective

a. a way of thinking about something that is influenced by the type of person you are or what you do.

b. do something that produces a change in someone or something

c. to collect written evidence

d. a result, or a reaction to something or someone

Use the academic words from the paragraph above to complete the sentences.

4. When Tom misbehaves in class, it has a bad _______________ on everyone.

5. If I don't get enough sleep, it will _______________ my mood.

6. When it comes to teamwork, Jana has a different _______________ than most people in the class because she is used to working alone.

7. She is writing an article that will _______________ the last presidential election.

Complete the sentences with your own ideas.

Example: A book or movie that had an effect on me was ___The Black Stallion___.

8. When I don't complete my homework, it can affect _______________.

9. When people want to hear my perspective on something, I feel _______________
_______________.

10. One day, I would like to document _______________.

Name ______________________________ Date ______________

WORD STUDY **Sound-Letter Relationships** *Use with textbook page 127.*

REMEMBER In English, the letter *s* has two different sounds. It can sound like a hissing snake */sss/* or a buzzing bee */zzz/*.

Choose /*sss*/ or /*zzz*/ for each word.

1. soldier
   a. /*sss*/ **b.** /*zzz*/
2. miles
   a. /*sss*/ **b.** /*zzz*/
3. cows
   a. /*sss*/ **b.** /*zzz*/
4. sunny
   a. /*sss*/ **b.** /*zzz*/
5. suit
   a. /*sss*/ **b.** /*zzz*/
6. Saturday
   a. /*sss*/ **b.** /*zzz*/

Write sentences using four of the words above.

7. ______________________________

8. ______________________________

9. ______________________________

10. ______________________________

READING STRATEGY RECOGNIZE HISTORICAL CONTEXT

Use with textbook page 127.

REMEMBER Analyzing the historical context of a story helps you understand it better. Historical context includes the culture, politics, and social setting for a particular group of people. It also includes the conditions in which they live.

Read this information about the Civil War and the period following it in the United States. Then answer the questions.

The issue of slavery divided the United States for many years in the late 1800s. The Civil War began in 1861 and ended in 1865. While slavery continued in the South during the war, thousands of African Americans fought with the Union Army of the North. In February 1865, President Lincoln signed an amendment to the Constitution outlawing slavery in the United States. The Civil War ended two months later.

In 1868, African Americans were given citizenship, and in 1870, it became illegal to deny a person the right to vote based on race. However, during the years between 1876, all the way through 1965, many states passed Jim Crow laws. These laws discriminated against African Americans. This was a difficult period because despite having citizenship, many African Americans were still not being treated equally. They were not able to vote, they had to go to separate schools, and they weren't aloud to sit with white people in public places.

1. What do you know about the period before, during, and after the Civil War in the United States?

   ____

2. Are you surprised that many African Americans fought with the Union Army? Do you think it was important? Explain.

   ____

3. In the United States, some laws are made for all the states, and some laws are made individually for each state. Can this be a problem? How?

   ____

4. How do you think life was during the time when Jim Crow laws were legal? Do you think some African-American people were treated more fairly than others?

   ____

5. How can the skill of analyzing historical context help you better understand what you read?

   ____

Name ______________________________ Date ______________

COMPREHENSION

Use with textbook page 134.

Choose the best answer for each item. Circle the letter of the correct answer.

1. James Welder was ______ the workers.

   a. nice to   **b.** mean to   **c.** quiet with

2. When Tony made the delivery in the big freeze, he worked hard to ______.

   a. ride the horse   **b.** keep the horse safe   **c.** help the cattle

3. Johnny Simpson thought that Tony ______.

   a. worked very hard   **b.** didn't like his job   **c.** should go to the dock

4. Tony ran home after he made thirty dollars because he ______.

   a. wanted more money   **b.** was tired   **c.** was happy

5. During the Depression, many people, including Tony, ______.

   a. had jobs on ranches   **b.** were old   **c.** were poor

RESPONSE TO LITERATURE

Use with textbook page 135.

Imagine that you are Tony. Do you think he had a good life or a hard life? Write a few lines, as Tony, describing how you feel.

____

____

____

____

____

____

____

____

____

____

GRAMMAR **Direct Quotations: Statements** *Use with textbook page 136.*

REMEMBER A direct quotation is enclosed in quotation marks (" ") at the beginning and at the end of the quotation. If the phrase identifying the speaker comes first, use a comma before the quotation and start the quotation with a capital letter.
Example: He said, "Let's go to the movies."
If the phrase identifying the speaker comes afterwards, a comma follows the quotation.
Example: "Let's go to the movies," he said.
If the quotation is interrupted, use quotation marks for both parts of the quotation.
Do not capitalize the second part of the quotation.
Example: "Well," he said, "it's raining today. Let's go to the movies."

Add the correct punctuation to these sentences.

1. Lucinda said I am going to change my name.
2. I will help you with your work Maria said.
3. We don't know said Mama if she is going to have dinner with us.
4. You aren't doing enough work the teacher said.
5. Billy said you didn't tell us about the test tomorrow.

Are these quotations correctly punctuated or not? Correct the mistakes.

	Correct	Incorrect
6. "It's not fair," said Mathew.	☐	☐
7. Gina said "Where are you taking us?"	☐	☐
8. Why don't you ask for help," he said when you're in trouble?	☐	☐
9. "It's too dark to see anything, said Frankie.	☐	☐
10. It's late," said her mother "and you have to go to bed now."	☐	☐

Name ______________________ Date ______________

Direct Quotations: Questions *Use with textbook page 137.*

REMEMBER Use a phrase with the reporting verb ask when you quote a question directly. A comma comes after the phrase if it comes first. Use a capital letter at the beginning and a question mark (?) at the end of the quotation. The final quotation marks come after the question mark.
Example: I asked, "Can I use your computer?"

Which sentence in each pair is correct? Mark the correct sentence with an X.

1. _____ I asked, "Where is the computer room?"

   _____ I asked, "Where is the computer room?

2. _____ "Is it time for lunch," they asked.

   _____ "Is it time for lunch?" they asked.

3. _____ Jessie asked, "can you help me?"

   _____ Jessie asked, "Can you help me?"

4. _____ "What time is it now?" The teacher asked.

   _____ "What time is it now?" the teacher asked.

5. _____ His father asked, Where are you going?"

   _____ His father asked, "Where are you going?"

Complete the sentences. Use the correct punctuation.

6. I asked my friend ______________________

7. My parents asked me ______________________

8. ______________________ my teacher asked.

9. ______________________ I asked.

WRITING **Write a Personal Narrative** *Use with textbook pages 138–139.*

Complete your own sequence-of-events chart for a personal narrative.

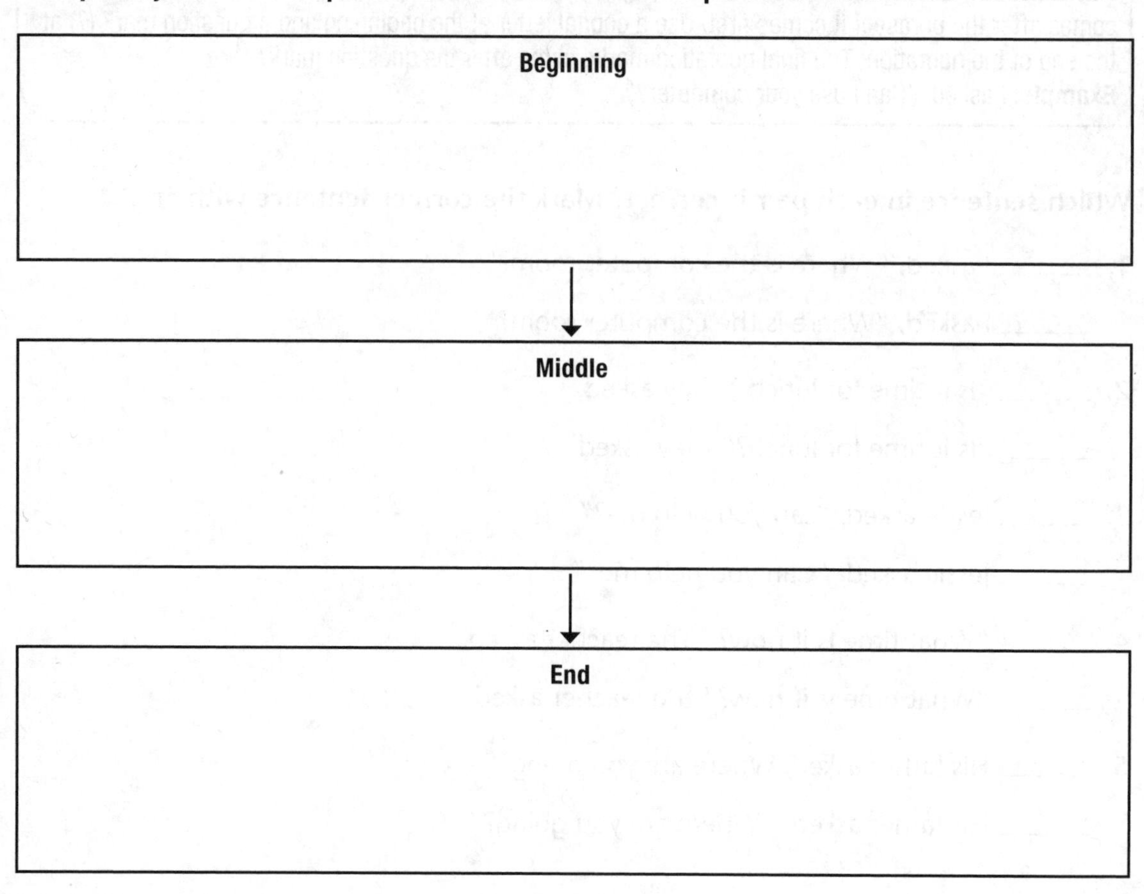

Use the Peer Review Checklist below to obtain feedback from your partner. This feedback will help you edit your final draft.

PEER REVIEW CHECKLIST

- ☐ Does the narrative tell about the writer's own experience?
- ☐ Does it hold the reader's interest and attention?
- ☐ Are events narrated with specificity and detail?
- ☐ Does the narrative have a beginning, middle, and end?
- ☐ Do quotations help bring individuals to life?
- ☐ What changes could be made to improve the narrative?

Name ________________________________ Date ______________

WRITING WORKSHOP

Use with textbook page 144.

Organize your ideas in the graphic organizer below.

CHARACTERS *Who?*	SETTING *Where?*	PROBLEM *What is the conflict?*	SOLUTION *What is the resolution?*

Use the Peer Review Checklist below to obtain feedback from your partner. This feedback will help you edit your final draft.

PEER REVIEW CHECKLIST

- ☐ Does the story build to a climax?
- ☐ Do precise words tell how the characters look, act, and feel?
- ☐ Is the setting believable?
- ☐ Are verbs, tenses, and pronoun/antecedents used correctly?
- ☐ Do sentences vary in length and pattern?
- ☐ What changes could be made to improve the essay?

LEARNING LOG *Use after completing page 148.*

Underline the vocabulary items you know and can use well. Review and practice any you haven't underlined. Underline them when you know them well.

Literary Words	Key Words	Academic Words	
dialogue	ancient	classical	benefit
setting	ceremony	cultural	category
point of view	citizen	feature	enormous
narrator	education	philosophy	percent
	rights	assist	affect
	rituals	bond	document
	average	conflict	effect
	conversion	process	perspective
	height		
	length		
	rate		
	weight		

Put a check by the skills you can perform well. Review and practice any you haven't checked off. Check them off when you can perform them well.

Skills	I can . . .
Word Study	☐ spell words with the long vowel sound /ē/. ☐ recognize and use suffixes *-ness, -tion,* and *-ation.* ☐ recognize and use animal verbs and idioms. ☐ spell words with the long vowel sound /ō/.
Reading Strategies	☐ compare and contrast. ☐ visualize. ☐ use visuals. ☐ recognize historical context.
Grammar	☐ show contrast using coordinating conjunctions and conjunctive adverbs. ☐ use count and non-count nouns and quantifiers. ☐ use simple past with regular and irregular verbs. ☐ use direct quotations.
Writing	☐ write a friendly letter. ☐ write about a character and setting. ☐ write a story from a different point of view. ☐ write a personal narrative. ☐ write a short story.

Test Preparation

TEST 1

DIRECTIONS
Read this selection. Then answer the questions that follow it.

Quinceañera

1 Almost every culture in the world has coming of age ceremonies. These ceremonies mark the time when children are recognized as adults. In Latin American countries, girls have a ceremony called the quinceañera. The ceremony is held on or near the girl's 15th birthday.

2 If the girl's family is religious, her special day will begin with a religious service. The family's religious leader will often be involved in some part of the ceremony. The girl may receive gifts of religious items, such as a rosary.

3 After the religious ceremony, the girl's family holds a celebration in their home or in another location such as a banquet hall. The girl will often carry a doll, which represents the last doll of her childhood. The girl's father will exchange her flat shoes for heels, at which time the girl will give her doll to her father. She then dances with her father and godfather. Soon the other guests dance as well. The event ends with everyone making toasts and eating cake.

1 The subject of this passage is ______.

A weddings
B quinceañera
C national holidays
D religious ceremonies

2 Why does the girl put on heels?

F To dress like an adult
G To dance with her father
H She likes high heels.
J To please her grandmother

TEST 2

DIRECTIONS
Read this selection. Then answer the questions that follow it.

In Water and On Land

1 Most animals change as they grow older. Some animals change colors while other animals grow larger. One special kind of animal grows new body parts and changes where it lives. This animal is an amphibian (am-FIB-ee-yuhn). Amphibians live in water at first, then later on land.

2 How do amphibians live in water and then live on land? First, all amphibians hatch from eggs. They are born in the water. They are born with gills and fins. They use their gills to breathe under water and their fins to swim.

3 When they are older, amphibians grow legs. They also grow lungs. Lungs are body parts that some animals use to breathe. The amphibians lose their gills and fins. Then they begin to live on land. They use their lungs to breathe and their legs to move on land.

1 What is paragraph 2 mainly about?

- **A** How amphibians live in water
- **B** How amphibians change as they grow
- **C** What kind of animals amphibians are
- **D** How amphibians live on land

2 The selection is best described as —

- **F** informative
- **G** humorous
- **H** entertaining
- **J** expressive

3 What does the word *lungs* mean?

- **A** Body parts that fish use to live on land
- **B** Body parts that amphibians use to swim
- **C** Body parts that animals use to breathe
- **D** Body parts that animals use to move on land

4 According to the selection, amphibians change as they grow because —

- **F** they use their fins to swim
- **G** they live in water and then they live on land
- **H** they use their lungs to breathe
- **J** they live on land and then live in water

Name ______________________________ Date ____________

TEST 3

DIRECTIONS
Read this selection. Then answer the questions that follow it.

Juan's Report

1 Juan could not believe his bad luck. It was the last day before spring vacation, and Mrs. Delgado gave them homework. He had to find facts about how animals change as they grow and write a report about what he learned. Suddenly, he had a thought. His sister Maria was in Mrs. Delgado's class last year. Maybe she could help him.

2 When Juan got home, he went upstairs to Maria's room. He knocked on the door. "Maria, can I come in?"

3 "Sure, Juan," Maria said.

4 Juan walked in and sat down in a chair. "Maria, I need your help. Mrs. Delgado assigned us a report. We have to find facts about how animals change as they grow. I have no idea where to start," Juan moaned.

5 "Juan, why don't you ask Mom to take you to the library? The librarian can help you find books full of interesting facts."

6 "Good idea, Maria!"

7 Juan went downstairs and asked his mom to take him to the library. When they got there, Juan asked the librarian where he could find books with facts about animals. She helped him find some books. Juan sat down with his stack and began to read.

8 Juan found out that <u>mammals</u>, a type of animal, change a lot as they grow. He read that most young mammals are helpless when they are born. Their parents have to take care of them. The parents give them food and shelter. They also protect them from animals that want to eat them. When the young are old enough, their parents teach them how to find food and shelter. Juan wrote down a list of facts and took them home.

9 That night Juan wrote his report. He was surprised that he really enjoyed the assignment. He learned a lot of new facts about animals. Now he understood why Maria liked reading so much. However, he would not be reading during the whole vacation. He had a baseball game tomorrow afternoon, but maybe he could read about more animals tomorrow night.

1 Look at this graphic organizer.

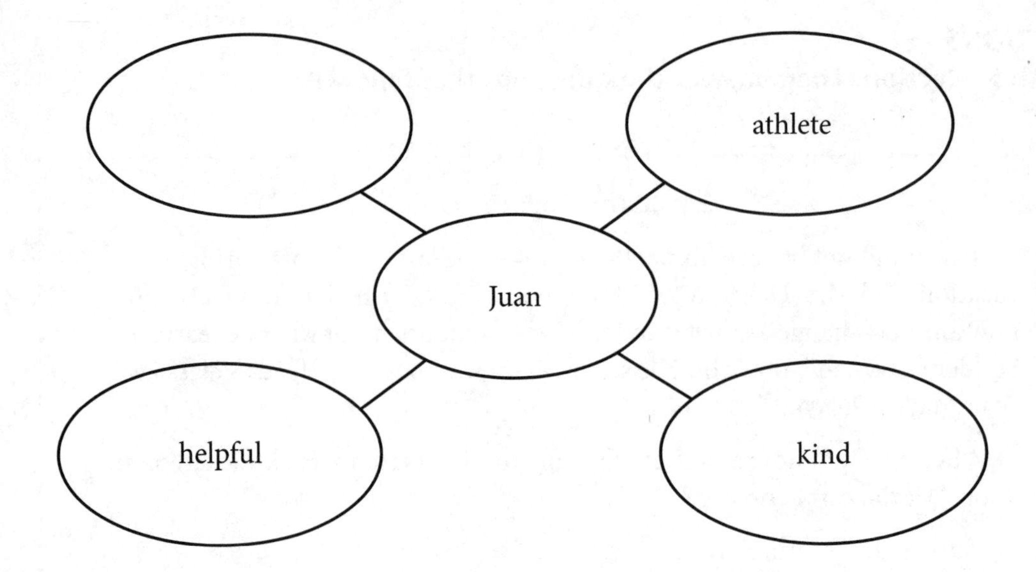

Which character trait best completes the web?

A funny
B lazy
C brave
D hardworking

2 Paragraph 8 is mainly about —

F how mammals change as they grow
G how different Maria is from Juan
H how Juan is unhappy about the assignment
J how Juan started working on his report

3 In paragraph 8, what words help the reader know what *mammals* means?

A helpless
B animals with hair and fur
C food and shelter
D a type of animal

4 According to the article, how do mammals change as they grow?

F They grow more hair.
G They learn to use gills to breathe.
H They learn to find food and shelter.
J They grow lungs and legs.

Name ______________________ Date ______________

Visual Literacy: Smithsonian American Art Museum *Use with textbook pages 150–151.*

LEARNING TO LOOK

Look at *The Lost Balloon* by William Holbrook Beard on page 151. Use that artwork to complete the web diagram below. For each "string" coming from the center, list one observation about the artwork.

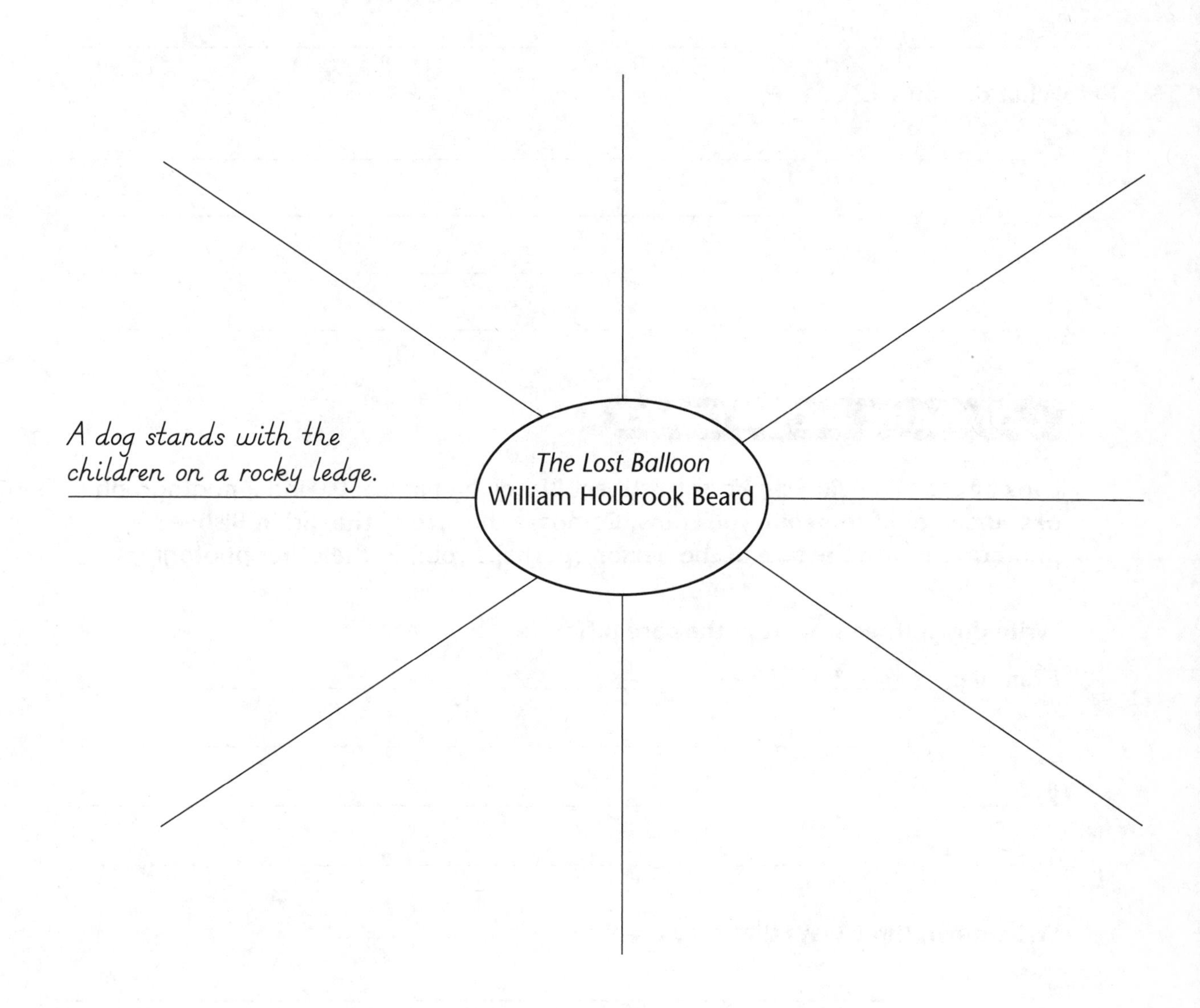

The Lost Balloon
William Holbrook Beard
A dog stands with the children on a rocky ledge.

INTERPRETATION

Look at *The Lost Balloon* by William Holbrook Beard again. Pretend you are one of the children in the painting.

What are you doing?

____

____

____

____

What do you see?

____

____

____

____

COMPARE & CONTRAST

Look at *Child on a Rocking Horse* by Albert Bisbee on page 150. Find a photograph of yourself or of someone you know. Compare the face of the girl in Bisbee's photograph with the face of the person (perhaps you!) in the other photograph.

Write down three ways that they are different.

Example: My face is larger.

1. ____

2. ____

3. ____

Write down three ways that they are similar.

4. ____

5. ____

6. ____

Name ______________________ Date ____________

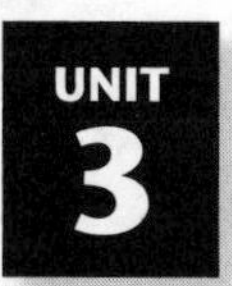

UNIT 3

How does helping others help us all?

READING 1: From *Run Away Home*

VOCABULARY Literary Words *Use with textbook page 155.*

REMEMBER Writers use **dialect** to show how people speak in a specific region. Often, writers create a **mood** or feeling in a story. One mood is **suspense**, which is uncertainty about what will happen.

Read each sentence. Write *Dialect* if the sentence contains dialect. Write *Mood* if the sentence has a mood. Write *Suspense* if the sentence contains suspense.

Dialect, Mood, or Suspense	Sentence
Mood	It was a dark, dreary night that made us feel sad.
1.	The heavy footsteps came nearer and nearer and stopped outside my room.
2.	"But of course you'd druther work, I reckon," Tom Sawyer said.
3.	Hector opened the big gift slowly as we all held our breath.
4.	The sun shone brightly, the birds sang sweetly, and the clouds looked like cotton candy.
5.	Huck said, "Oh, don't be afeared b'cause we ain't causin' no harm."

Read the story "The Big Test." Six parts are underlined. Label each underlined part as Suspense, Dialect, or Mood. The first example is done for you.

Mood

It was a gloomy and depressing winter day. Everyone in class waited to hear what Ms. Chin the teacher would say. Ms. Chin just stared at the class. The ticking clock sounded very loud. (8.)

(6.) Finally, Rita said, "Ma'am, do you'all know how we did on the big test?"

Still Ms. Chin said nothing. The kids held their breath. Some felt like they were going to scream with the tension! (9.)

(7.) Brad said, "Gollee! Pleeze tell us already!"

"You all passed!" Mrs. Chin shouted. The kids smiled in joy and cheered happily. (10.)

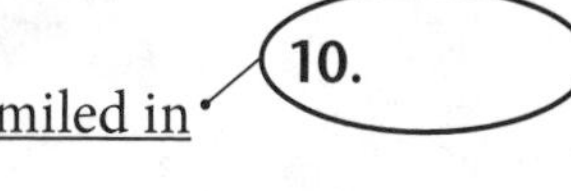

VOCABULARY **Academic Words** *Use with textbook page 156.*

Read the paragraph below. Pay attention to the underlined academic words.

> There are no precise rules about how to thank someone for a gift. However, it is important that you communicate your appreciation for the gift as soon as possible. If you are sending a thank-you note, it's most appropriate to send it the first week after receiving the gift. It is considered rude to let an extended period of time pass before sending a thank-you note.

Write the academic words from the paragraph above next to their correct definitions.

Example: *appropriate*: suitable for a particular time, situation, or purpose

1. ____________: a particular length of time in history or in a person's life
2. ____________: exact and correct in every detail
3. ____________: express your thoughts and feelings so that others understand them

Use the academic words from the paragraph above to complete the sentences.

4. People ____________ with movements as well as words.
5. It is ____________ to carry an umbrella when it is likely to rain.
6. Julio's watch is ____________, so he always arrives on time.
7. The nineteenth century was a ____________ of great progress in America.

Complete the sentences with your own ideas.

Example: I like to communicate with *email and text messages*.

8. My favorite period of American history is ____________.
9. I think it is important to be precise about ____________.
10. It is appropriate to buy a gift when ____________.

Name ______________________________ Date ______________

WORD STUDY **Uses of the Apostrophe** *Use with textbook page 157.*

REMEMBER An apostrophe is used to show where letters have been left out in a contraction. For example, the words *I* and *am* can be shortened to form the contraction *I'm*. An apostrophe is also used in dialect to show where letters are missing, as in the expression *yo'* for *you*.

Look at the chart below. Form the contraction for each pair of words. Write the contraction in the chart.

Word #1	Word #2	Contraction
would	not	wouldn't
1. you	will	
2. are	not	
3. who	is	
4. we	are	
5. she	is	

Look at the chart below. Write the word that each example of dialect represents. The dialect is underlined.

Dialect	Word
6. 'Deed, I do believe what you say is true.	
7. What are you thinkin' of doing now?	
8. Take off your gloves and put 'em down.	
9. I have had 'bout enough of your tricks!	
10. I s'pose I could help you out tomorrow.	

READING STRATEGY MAKE INFERENCES

Use with textbook page 157.

REMEMBER When you read, make inferences by trying to understand what the author means but does not say directly. Use clues in the text and your own experiences to make inferences.

Read each paragraph and answer the questions that follow.

Rob had been playing hockey since he was 5. He dreamed of being named captain of the team. He practiced all winter long. When the coach announced that another player would be captain of the team, Rob was upset. The coach said, "Rob—you're still an important player on the team." Rob replied, "I only cared about being captain. Now I'm not sure I even want to play."

1. What can you infer about Rob's character from the passage above?

____

____

2. What clues in the text helped you to make an inference about Rob's character?

____

____

Rita and Mia were working on a science project together. They agreed to split the work in half and each do their part. When the project was due, Rita had completed hers, but Mia had not even started hers. Mia said, "Well, we can tell the teacher that we both completed the first half of the project and then ran out of time."

3. What can you infer about Mia's character from the passage above?

____

____

4. What clues in the text helped you to make an inference about Mia's character?

____

____

5. How do you think making inferences can help you to read with better comprehension?

____

____

Name ______________________________ Date ______________

COMPREHENSION *Use with textbook page 164.*

Choose the best answer for each item. Circle the letter of the correct answer.

1. Sky is ill because he has _______.

   a. swamp fever **b.** quinine **c.** many mosquito bites

2. Sky escaped because _______.

   a. he wants to leave the country **b.** he didn't want to go to school in Pennsylvania **c.** he had to find his family

3. The message *the quilt is torn* means that _______.

   a. Sky ran away **b.** Sky got better **c.** Sky died

4. Mr. Wratten wants to help Sky because _______.

   a. he feels sorry for him **b.** he will get money **c.** he is his father

5. Papa gets Sky to _______.

   a. eat all the pork **b.** tell the truth about his past **c.** act with respect

RESPONSE TO LITERATURE *Use with textbook page 165.*

Write a paragraph that tells what you think will happen next in the story. Use dialogue to show the speaker's exact words. Write at least five lines.

____

____

____

____

____

____

____

____

GRAMMAR Agreement in Simple Sentences

Use with textbook page 166.

REMEMBER A simple sentence must contain a subject and verb. The verb must agree in number with the subject.
Example: He speak**s** Spanish. He **does**n't speak Apache.

Underline the subject and circle the verb in each sentence. Is the subject singular or plural?

	Singular	Plural
1. The boy doesn't speak Spanish.	☐	☐
2. He likes cool dry weather.	☐	☐
3. The horses are waiting outside.	☐	☐
4. A plate of cookies is on the table.	☐	☐
5. The oranges in the kitchen smell good.	☐	☐

Complete the sentences with the simple present of the verb in parentheses.

6. Sarah ____________________ in Alabama. (live)

7. Sarah and her mother ____________________ a young Apache boy. (find)

8. The boy ____________________ feel good. (not, feel)

9. ____________________ the boy ____________________ English? (speak)

10. The man with the horse ____________________ to send the boy away. (not, want)

Name ______________________________ Date ______________

Agreement in Compound Sentences *Use with textbook page 167.*

REMEMBER A compound sentence is two simple sentences, or independent clauses, joined with a coordinating conjunction such as *and, but,* or *so.* The verb tense in both clauses must agree. A comma is usually used before the coordinating conjunction.
Example: The boy *spoke,* and the girl *answered.*
Pronouns must also agree with their antecedents (the noun that comes before them).
Example: *The boy* was awake, but *he* couldn't speak.

Match the sentences below. Then rewrite them as complete sentences. Use the correct punctuation.

1. Her parents were worried. (so)
2. My brother doesn't study hard. (but)
3. Our cats don't like milk. (so)
4. The bus was late. (and)
5. The girl wore a coat. (but)

a. She didn't have a hat.
b. It was very crowded.
c. They called the school.
d. He gets good grades.
e. They drink water.

1. ______________________________
2. ______________________________
3. ______________________________
4. ______________________________
5. ______________________________

Form a compound sentence by writing a simple sentence after each coordinating conjunction.

6. The boy was sick, and ______________________________
7. We gave the boy some soup, so ______________________________
8. The boy woke up, but ______________________________

WRITING **Write a Book Review** *Use with textbook pages 168–169.*

Complete your own opinion-reasons chart for a review of a book or story that you like very much.

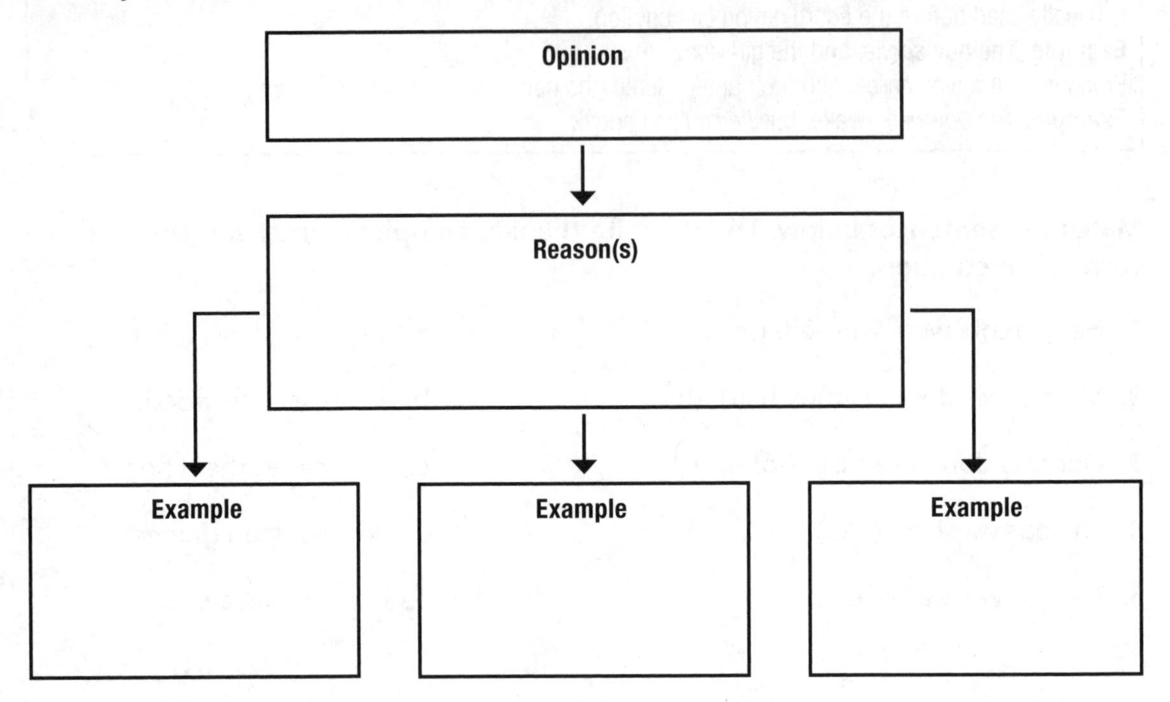

Use the Peer Review Checklist below to obtain feedback from your partner. This feedback will help you edit your final draft.

PEER REVIEW CHECKLIST

- ☐ Does the review state the writer's opinion about a book?
- ☐ Do reasons and examples support the writer's opinion?
- ☐ Are reasons and examples presented in a logical order?
- ☐ Is the writing voice strong and persuasive?
- ☐ Do sentences vary in length and pattern?
- ☐ What changes could be made to improve the review?

Name ______________________________ Date ______________

How does helping others help us all?

READING 2: "Extraordinary People: Serving Others"

VOCABULARY **Key Words** *Use with textbook page 171.*

Write each word in the box next to its definition.

assassinated	extraordinary	founders	resistance	superintendent	tolerance

Example: _tolerance_: willingness to allow people to do, say, or believe what they want

1. ____________: people who establish a business, organization, school, etc.
2. ____________: very unusual, special, or surprising
3. ____________: refusal to accept new ideas or changes
4. ____________: murdered (an important person)
5. ____________: someone who is responsible for a place, job, activity, etc.

Use the words in the box at the top of the page to complete the sentences.

6. We celebrate the town ____________ every year by holding a parade in their honor.
7. The motto "live and let live" shows ____________.
8. The mules showed their ____________ by refusing to move!
9. World War I started when a royal leader in Europe was ____________.
10. Comic book heroes always have ____________ powers, such as super speed.

VOCABULARY **Academic Words** *Use with textbook page 172.*

Read the paragraph below. Pay attention to the underlined academic words.

> My soccer coach has played a positive role in my life. He helped me alter my exercise and practice routine. The changes made a strong impact on my soccer skills. I was named team captain by mid-season. My coach helped me achieve this goal.

Write the letter of the correct definition next to each word.

Example: ___c___ achieve

_______ **1.** alter

_______ **2.** impact

_______ **3.** role

a. change in some way

b. the position, job, or function someone or something has in a particular situation or activity

c. succeed in doing or getting something as a result of your actions

d. the effect that something or someone has on someone or something

Use the academic words from the exercise above to complete the sentences.

4. The weather has a big _______________ on her feelings.

5. John has a starring _______________ in the play.

6. One of the best ways to _______________ your goals is through hard work.

7. Rick can never decide what to do, so he will often _______________ his plans at the last minute.

Complete the sentences with your own ideas.

Example: Pets can play an important role in *helping blind people*.

8. The person who has had the biggest impact on my life is

_______________________.

9. One thing I would like to alter about my daily life is

_______________________.

10. The goals I plan to achieve include _______________________.

Name ______________________________ Date ______________

WORD STUDY Spelling Words with Silent *gh*

Use with textbook page 173.

REMEMBER In English, the letters *gh* are often silent, but not always. For example, the letters *gh* are silent in the word *though*, but they stand for the sound /g/ in the word *ghostly*. Knowing when the letters *gh* are silent will help you spell and pronounce words correctly.

Read the words in the box below. Then write each word in the correct column in the chart.

~~weight~~	spaghetti	ghost	straight	gherkin
tight	ghetto	ghastly	through	ought

Silent *gh*	*gh* stands for /g/
weight	

Write "silent gh" next to the words that have a silent *gh*. Write "/g/" next to any words in which the letters *gh* stand for the sound /g/.

Example: though ___silent gh___

1. slight ______________

2. slaughter ______________

3. Ghana ______________

4. thigh ______________

5. eight ______________

6. high ______________

READING STRATEGY IDENTIFY PROBLEMS AND SOLUTIONS

Use with textbook page 173.

REMEMBER When you read, try to identify problems and solutions. A problem is a challenge that a person, group, or character faces. A solution is how the person, group, or character fixes the problem.

Read each paragraph. Then answer the questions that follow.

Gemma forgot her lunch money. She had no idea how she was going to pay for lunch. She called her parents but they couldn't come to school and bring her money. Then her best friend offered to share her lunch with Gemma. There was more than enough for both of them.

1. What is the problem in the passage above?

____

____

2. What is the solution in the passage above?

____

____

Oscar was failing at science class. He found it very difficult and did not know what to do. Then the science teacher offered to tutor him after class. Oscar worked with his science teacher, and in a few weeks, his grades were much better.

3. What is the problem in the passage above?

____

____

4. What is the solution to the problem?

____

____

5. How do you think the strategy of identifying a problem and a solution will make you a better reader?

____

____

Name ______________________ Date ____________

COMPREHENSION

Use with textbook page 178.

Choose the best answer for each item. Circle the letter of the correct answer.

1. Benito Juárez is famous for ______.

   a. starting a nursing school
   b. serving as a president of Mexico who made many reforms
   c. using passive resistance

2. Florence Nightingale was called ______.

   a. "mother to millions"
   b. "England's helper"
   c. "the lady with the lamp"

3. The international symbol of nonviolent protest is ______.

   a. Doctors without Borders
   b. Mohandas Gandhi
   c. Helen Keller

4. Franklin Delano Roosevelt is ranked as one of America's greatest presidents because ______.

   a. he helped the nation through very difficult times
   b. he started hospitals
   c. he had polio

5. Helen Keller is celebrated today for ______.

   a. leading nations
   b. giving medical care
   c. inspiring handicapped people

EXTENSION

Use with textbook page 179.

Think about famous people you have heard about. Write why they are famous and why you admire them.

Person or Group	Why Famous	Why I Admire the Person

GRAMMAR Prepositions of Time: *in, on,* and *at*

Use with textbook page 180.

REMEMBER The prepositions *in, on,* and *at* refer to points in time. Use *in* before months, years, centuries, and seasons.
Examples: in May; in 1776; in the twenty-first century; in winter
Use *on* before days and exact dates.
Examples: on Tuesday; on July 4
Use *at* before times of day.
Example: at nine o'clock

Complete the chart with items from the box. Write each word or phrase under the preposition it's used with.

June	midnight	Monday	Thanksgiving	the summer
March 4	8:15 A.M.	the tenth century	seven o'clock	1984

in	
1.	3.
2.	4.
on	**at**
5.	8.
6.	9.
7.	10.

Complete each sentence with *in, on,* or *at*.

Example: The United States won its independence ___*in*___ the eighteenth century.

11. The United States declared its independence ________ July 4, 1776.

12. We observe the birthday of Martin Luther King Jr. ________ January.

13. The movie will be on television tonight ________ eight o'clock.

14. The new year begins ________ midnight.

15. Thanksgiving is always celebrated ________ a Thursday.

Name ______________________________ Date ______________

Prepositional Phrases Providing Details *Use with textbook page 181.*

REMEMBER Prepositional phrases can give more details to a sentence. The prepositional phrase can describe a noun, a verb, or an adjective.
Example: She became sick *with a fever.*
(The phrase provides details about the word *sick*.)

Underline the prepositional phrase in each sentence. Does it describe a noun, a verb, or an adjective?

1. Ghandi was born in the western part of India. ___Verb___
2. In 1893, he traveled to South Africa. ______________
3. A group of white South Africans attacked him. ______________
4. Gandhi became a leader in India's struggle for independence. ______________
5. Indians were angry with the British rule of India. ______________
6. Ghandi became a symbol of nonviolent protest. ______________

Choose the best preposition to complete each sentence.

about	after	among	before	by	for	from	in	near	on	out	to	under	up	with

7. Juarez was the son of poor Zapotec farmers ______________ the state of Oaxaca.
8. Florence Nightingale came ______________ a wealthy family.
9. Roosevelt was elected as the 32nd president ______________ the United States.
10. Doctors Without Borders is an organization that works to tell the world ______________ people who are sick and suffering.

WRITING Write a Persuasive Paragraph

Use with textbook pages 182–183.

Complete your own question-and-answer chart for a paragraph about someone you think is truly extraordinary. Answer the question *"What extraordinary things did this person do?"*

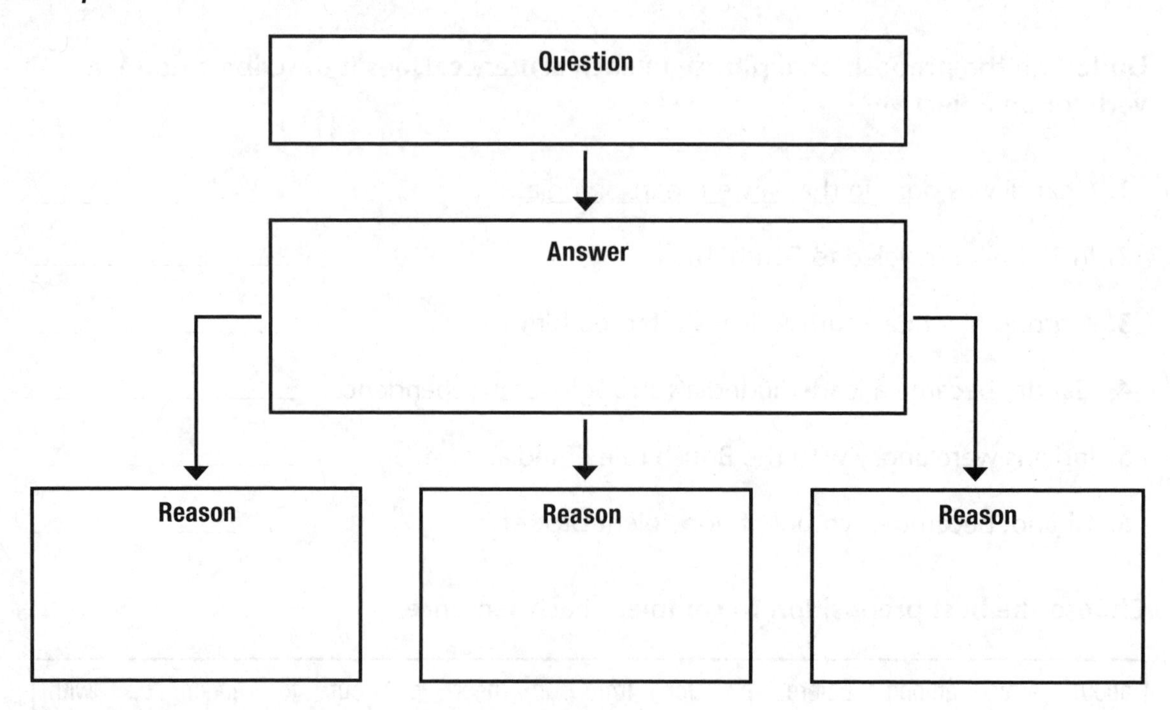

Use the Peer Review Checklist below to obtain feedback from your partner. This feedback will help you edit your final draft.

PEER REVIEW CHECKLIST

- ☐ Does the paragraph ask a question and answer it persuasively?
- ☐ Does the writer state a clear opinion?
- ☐ Is the writer's opinion supported by facts, details, and examples?
- ☐ Do strong and persuasive words appeal to readers' emotions?
- ☐ Are prepositions of time used correctly?
- ☐ What changes could be made to improve the paragraph?

Name ______________________ Date __________

How does helping others help us all?

READING 3: From *Zlata's Diary*

VOCABULARY **Literary Words** *Use with textbook page 185.*

REMEMBER A **figure of speech** is a group of words or phrases that do not match the literal, or dictionary definition, of the words.
Example: The steak was as tough as nails.
Hyperbole is a figure of speech that uses exaggeration, or overstatement.
Example: I'm so hungry that I could eat a whole cow!

Read each sentence. Write *figure of speech* if the sentence has a figure of speech. If the figure of speech is a hyperbole, write *hyperbole*.

Literary Words	Sentence
hyperbole	The joke was so funny that José nearly died laughing.
1.	The math test was as easy as pie.
2.	The model wore at least 100 pounds of makeup.
3.	It's 1,000 degrees outside.
4.	I'm so tired that I could sleep for a year.
5.	That sofa cost an arm and a leg.

Write sentences using the literary elements listed.

Literary Element	Sentence
Figure of speech	*Jack is always pulling our leg with his jokes.*
6. Hyperbole	
7. Figure of speech	
8. Hyperbole	
9. Figure of speech	
10. Hyperbole	

VOCABULARY **Academic Words** *Use with textbook page 186.*

Read the paragraph below. Pay attention to the underlined academic words.

All of us suffer from stress at times. Experts say that the best method for fighting stress is to establish a healthy lifestyle. The basics of a healthy lifestyle include a diet that should consist of healthy, balanced foods, at least one hour of exercise a day, and between seven and nine hours of sleep a night.

Write the academic words from the paragraph above next to their correct definitions.

Example: ___*stress*___: continuous feelings of worry caused by difficulties in your life

1. ________________: are made up of or contain particular things or people
2. ________________: create; organize
3. ________________: a planned way of doing something

Use the academic words from the paragraph above to complete the sentences.

4. I always feel ________________ before a big test.
5. The class wants to ________________ a scholarship fund.
6. Luis has his own ________________ for raking leaves.
7. The meal will ________________ of foods from many countries.

Complete the sentences with your own ideas.

Example: I feel stress when ___*I oversleep in the morning*___.

8. My birthday party will consist of ________________.
9. I would like to establish a club that ________________.
10. My method for cleaning my room is ________________.

Name ______________________________ Date ______________

WORD STUDY **Synonyms and Antonyms** *Use with textbook page 187.*

REMEMBER Synonyms are words with the same or nearly the same meaning, such as *error* and *mistake*. Antonyms are words that have opposite or nearly opposite meanings, such as *hot* and *cold*. You can use context clues, including synonyms and antonyms, to figure out words that you don't know.

Read the sentences in the chart below. Underline the context clues that help you figure out the meaning of each boldfaced word. Then identify the type of the clue you found. Write the clue word in the second column of the chart, and label it *synonym* or *antonym*.

Sentences with Unfamiliar Words	Type of Context Clue
During the war, everyday items that once were cheap became very **expensive**.	*cheap = antonym*
1. Zlata felt very unsafe during the war. She and her family faced many **hazardous** situations.	
2. Neighbors who were friends a year ago are now **enemies**.	
3. In order to **defend** ourselves, we had to know when the bombers were going to attack.	
4. During the war, I read newspapers because I wanted to know the facts. I didn't want to read any **fiction**.	
5. The bridge was **damaged** during the conflict, but later it was repaired.	

Read each sentence. Underline words or phrases that are clues to meaning. Then write your own definition of each boldfaced term.

Example: Although I **nagged** him, he was never annoyed by my questions.

nagged = asked annoying questions

6. Today the ocean is calm again; it looks as **tranquil** as a sheet of glass.

____

7. The market is **bustling** from Monday to Friday, but it is quiet on the weekend.

____

8. My sister has no sense of **decorum**. Her rude behavior upsets me.

____

READING STRATEGY DISTINGUISH FACT FROM OPINION

Use with textbook page 187.

REMEMBER When you read, distinguish fact from opinion. A fact is a statement that can be proven. An opinion is a person's point of view about a topic. Opinions are not necessarily wrong, but they can't be proven.

Read each pair of statements. Then answer the questions that follow.

Carrots are full of vitamins. I think they taste great.

1. Which statement is a fact?

____

____

2. Which statement is an opinion?

____

____

Flowers come in many colors. I love them!

3. Which statement is a fact?

____

____

4. Which statement is an opinion?

____

____

5. How can the strategy of distinguishing between fact and opinion help you become a better reader?

____

____

____

____

Name ______________________________ Date ______________

COMPREHENSION

Use with textbook page 194.

Choose the best answer for each item. Circle the letter of the correct answer.

1. Zlata's diary is about _______.

   a. only herself **b.** her mother "Mimmy" **c.** the war in Sarajevo

2. In her entry on May 26, Zlata wants to _______.

   a. move away for good **b.** learn to speak English **c.** give her friend a birthday gift

3. Vaso Miskin Street is _______.

   a. the scene of many bombs and death **b.** where Zlata lives **c.** where Zlata's dad works

4. As winter comes to the town, people _______.

   a. celebrate peace **b.** lack water and electricity **c.** play games with kids

5. Zlata's parents _______.

   a. get thin and sad **b.** decide to get new jobs **c.** play the piano for fun

RESPONSE TO LITERATURE

Use with textbook page 195.

Read the dates from Zlata's diary. First read what happened each day. Then write what you might do or how you might feel if you were in Zlata's place.

Saturday
May 23 ______________________________

Tuesday
May 26 ______________________________

Wednesday
May 27 ______________________________

Thursday
October 1 ______________________________

Monday
December 28 ______________________________

GRAMMAR Placement of Adjectives *Use with textbook pages 196–197.*

REMEMBER An adjective describes a noun or noun phrase. An adjective often comes right before the noun it describes.
Example: That is a big dog.
An adjective can also appear after a linking verb such as *be*, *get*, *become*, *seem*, or *look*.
Example: That dog is big.

Choose the best adjective to complete each sentence.

angry	close	cold	terrible	true

1. Zlata wrote about the ________________ war in her country.
2. Everything she wrote was ________________.
3. She sometimes felt ________________.
4. Her family needed wood for the ________________ winter.
5. Many of their ________________ friends were killed.

Circle the adjective in each sentence.

6. I was so unhappy because of the war.
7. Maja is my best friend.
8. I am lucky to have my friends.
9. I made a little present for Mirna.
10. I felt disappointed that I couldn't see her.

Name ______________________________ Date ______________

Placement of Adjectives *Use with textbook pages 196–197.*

REMEMBER You can use a possessive noun, such as *Zlata's*, or a possessive adjective, such as *my, your, their,* etc., before an adjective.
Example: My best friend is Lucia.
You can also use the pronouns *this, that, these,* or *those* before an adjective.
Example: These new shoes are very uncomfortable.

Add the word in parentheses to the correct place in each sentence.

1. This is an book that everyone should read. (important)
2. A young girl wrote touching diary. (this)
3. After reading this diary, you can understand angry feelings. (her)
4. Zlata's story reaches across all ages and all countries. (moving)

How many sentences can you make from the words in the box? You can use the words as many times as you want.

this	interesting	books	is	are
these	book	important	an	

____

____

____

____

____

WRITING **Write a Diary Entry** *Use with textbook pages 198–199.*

Complete your own T-chart for a diary entry about an important issue in the world.

ISSUE	
For	**Against**

Use the Peer Review Checklist below to obtain feedback from your partner. This feedback will help you edit your final draft.

PEER REVIEW CHECKLIST

- ☐ Does the diary entry examine both sides of an issue?
- ☐ Is the writer's opinion about the issue stated clearly?
- ☐ Is the writer's opinion supported by good reasons?
- ☐ Does the writing voice express the writer's feelings?
- ☐ Are adjectives placed in the correct order?
- ☐ What changes could be made to improve the paragraph?

Name ______________________ Date ______________

How does helping others help us all?

READING 4: "Friendship and Cooperation in the Animal Kingdom"

VOCABULARY **Key Words** *Use with textbook page 201.*

Write each word in the box next to its definition.

arrangement	cooperate	damage	gigantic	intruder	tsunami

Example: tsunami : a very large ocean wave caused by an underwater earthquake

1. ______________: physical harm that is done to something
2. ______________: work together with someone else to achieve something
3. ______________: extremely large
4. ______________: something that has been organized or agreed on
5. ______________: someone who enters an area where he or she is not supposed to be

Use the words in the box at the top of the page to complete the sentences.

6. When we ______________, our chores get done faster because everyone helps out.
7. Dolphins are small, not ______________.
8. The ______________ looked like a wall of water crashing down on the village.
9. My mother has a(n) ______________ with a neighbor who takes in our mail.
10. Any crash will ______________ a car.

VOCABULARY Academic Words *Use with textbook page 202.*

Read the paragraph below. Pay attention to the underlined academic words.

The World Kindness Movement was formed in 1997 by a group in Japan who wanted to spread the concept of kindness. They believe that having a positive attitude and doing kind things for others can help improve a community. Acts of kindness can be as simple as thanking the people we rely on every day, such as firefighters and police officers. One may comment that being nice isn't so hard, and the World Kindness Movement hopes that everyone sees it that way.

Write the letter of the correct definition next to each word.

Example: __b__ rely on

______ **1.** concept

______ **2.** attitude

______ **3.** comment

a. a stated opinion made about someone or something

b. trust or depend on someone or something

c. an idea of how something is or how something should be done

d. the opinions and feelings that you usually have about someone or something

Use the academic words from the exercise above to complete the sentences.

4. We did not hear the ________________ because the speaker's voice was too soft.

5. The teacher explained the ________________ of supply-and-demand so that I could understand the idea.

6. Babies ________________ their parents for all their needs.

7. Lina has a negative ________________ toward spinach.

Complete the sentences with your own ideas.

Example: We have a good attitude about __moving to a new place__.

8. In my diary, I will write a comment about ________________________.

9. In science, I study the concept of ________________________.

10. We rely on rain for ________________________.

Name ______________________ Date ____________

WORD STUDY **Greek and Latin Roots** *Use with textbook page 203.*

REMEMBER Many English words come from ancient Greek or Latin word parts, called roots. For example, the word *auto* is a Greek root meaning "self." An automatic machine is one that "works by itself." Knowing the meaning of common Greek and Latin roots can help you figure out the meanings of many English words.

Look at the chart below. Then add words from the box to the correct row on the chart.

~~asteroid~~	dictator	pedal	pedestrian	podiatrist	podium	predict

Root	Meaning	Origin	English Words
aster/astro	star	Greek	astronomical asteroid
pous/podos	foot	Greek	octopus **1.** ____________ **2.** ____________
ped/pedis	foot	Latin	centipede **3.** ____________ **4.** ____________
dict	say; speak	Latin	dictate **5.** ____________ **6.** ____________

Choose the word from the box below that best completes each sentence.

~~asteroid~~	podiatrist	predict	pedestrian	podium

Example: An asteroid is a large object made of rock that moves about in space.

7. A doctor who takes care of people's feet is called a ____________.

8. Fortune tellers try to ____________, or say in advance, what will happen.

9. When you give a speech, you often stand at a tall narrow desk called a ____________.

10. Someone who is walking instead of driving is called a ____________.

READING STRATEGY IDENTIFY MAIN IDEAS AND DETAILS

Use with textbook page 203.

REMEMBER When you read, identify the main idea and details. The main idea is the most important idea in a passage. Details are small pieces of information that support the main idea.

Read each paragraph. Then answer the questions that follow.

The year is divided into seasons. Each season has its own type of weather. There are four seasons in a year. The seasons are spring, summer, fall, and winter. Each season lasts about three months.

1. What is the main idea of the passage above?

____

____

2. What are the details that support the main idea?

____

____

Using a homework planner is a great way to stay organized. Everytime you are in class, write down the homework in your homework planner. Then, when you are doing your homework, take out your planner. You will have all of your assignments neatly written down in one place.

3. What is the main idea of the passage above?

____

____

4. What are the details that support the main idea?

____

____

5. How can identifying the main idea and details help you to read with greater comprehension?

____

____

Name ______________________ Date ______________

COMPREHENSION *Use with textbook page 208.*

Choose the best answer for each item. Circle the letter of the correct answer.

1. The plover and the crocodile ______.

a. help each other **b.** ignore each other **c.** harm each other

2. Owen is a hippo who became best friends with a ______.

a. bird **b.** wise man **c.** tortoise

3. Owen was separated from his mother by a ______.

a. group of hippos **b.** tsunami **c.** hunter

4. People took Owen to a(n) ______.

a. coral reef **b.** different ocean **c.** animal shelter

5. The main idea of this article is that animals ______.

a. are different from people **b.** can become friends **c.** are wild creatures

EXTENSION *Use with textbook page 209.*

Write the names of five animals in the chart below. Then research how these animals help people or other animals.

Animal	How the Animal Helps People or Other Animals
dogs	*help blind people get around*

GRAMMAR Participial Adjectives *Use with textbook page 210.*

REMEMBER The present participle, the *-ing* form of a verb, and the past participle, often formed with *-ed*, can be used as adjectives. A present participial adjective modifies the noun that performs the action; it describes the cause of the feeling.
Example: These wild animals are *fascinating.*
A past participial adjective can be restated with a *by* phrase; it describes the receiver of the feeling.
Example: I am *fascinated* by these wild animals.

Complete each sentence with a participial adjective (*-ing* or *-ed*) made from the verb in parentheses.

1. The land is already ______________ by wildlife. (inhabit)
2. Drivers can be ______________ by the appearance of wildlife. (surprise)
3. Some ______________ species of wild animals are disappearing. (amaze)
4. The mountain lions are ______________ by the new cities. (endanger)
5. The plans for these new cities are ______________. (worry)

Circle the correct word to complete the sentences.

6. We saw a very (exciting / excited) movie last weekend.
7. We were (frustrating / frustrated) because the rain stopped us from playing soccer.
8. The students were (confused / confusing) by the new school rules.
9. Everyone was (bored / boring) by his story.
10. The story's ending was very (surprised / surprising).

Name ______________________________ Date ______________

Prepositions of Location *Use with textbook page 211.*

> **REMEMBER** A preposition shows location or time. Some common prepositions of location are *under, below, in, behind, after, near, beneath, above, beside, between, on, across,* and *outside.*
> **Example:** Please don't put the book on the table.

Complete each sentence with a word from the box.

behind	between	outside	below	on

1. He put a slice of cheese ______________ two slices of bread to make a sandwich.
2. Europe lies ______________ the Atlantic Ocean.
3. The roots of a tree lie ______________ the ground.
4. The ducklings waddled ______________ their mother, following her to the pond.
5. Inside the house it was quiet, but a great deal was going on ______________ the window.

Write a sentence with the prepositional phrase in parentheses.

Example: (after another) *The students lined up one after another.*

6. (next to me)

____

7. (beneath his name)

____

8. (beside the chair)

____

9. (in a suitcase)

____

10. (on the roof)

____

WRITING **Write a Critical Evaluation** *Use with textbook pages 212–213.*

Complete your own outline for a critical evaluation of a person or issue.

I. Main Idea (introduce standards)

A.

B.

C.

II. Main Idea (judge topic)

A.

B.

C.

Use the Peer Review Checklist below to obtain feedback from your partner. This feedback will help you edit your final draft.

PEER REVIEW CHECKLIST

- ☐ Does the critical evaluation focus on a person or issue?
- ☐ Does it provide a set of standards for judging the topic?
- ☐ Do strong examples support the writer's judgment?
- ☐ Do sentences vary in length and pattern?
- ☐ Are comparisons with *less* and *least* used correctly?
- ☐ What changes could be made to improve the paragraph?

Name ______________________________ Date ____________

WRITING WORKSHOP

Use with textbook page 218.

Organize your ideas in the graphic organizer below.

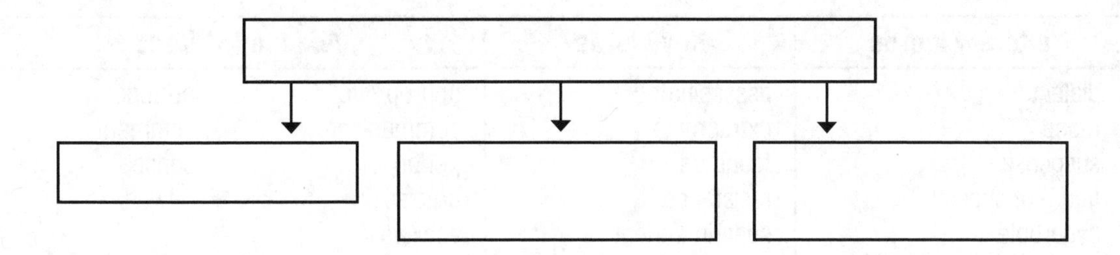

Use the Peer Review Checklist below to obtain feedback from your partner. This feedback will help you edit your final draft.

PEER REVIEW CHECKLIST

- ☐ Does the speech have an introduction and conclusion?
- ☐ Does it include signal words such as *I believe* and *I think*?
- ☐ Are reasons and examples presented in an order that makes sense?
- ☐ Does the writing have energy and show the writer's personality?
- ☐ Are prepositions of time used correctly?
- ☐ What changes could be made to improve the essay?

LEARNING LOG

Use after completing page 222.

Underline the vocabulary items you know and can use well. Review and practice any you haven't underlined. Underline them when you know them well.

Literary Words	Key Words	Academic Words	
dialect mood suspense figure of speech hyperbole	assassinated extraordinary founders resistance superintendent tolerance endangered species extinct habitat prime residence subdivision	appropriate communicate period precise achieve alter impact role consist establish method stress	attitude comment concept rely on

Put a check by the skills you can perform well. Review and practice any you haven't checked off. Check them off when you can perform them well.

Skills	I can . . .
Word Study	☐ use apostrophes. ☐ recognize and spell words with silent *gh*. ☐ recognize and use synonyms and antonyms. ☐ recognize and use consonant clusters.
Reading Strategies	☐ make inferences. ☐ identify problems and solutions. ☐ distinguish fact from opinion. ☐ identify main idea and details.
Grammar	☐ use agreement in simple and compound sentences. ☐ use prepositions of time *in, on, at* and prepositional phrases providing details. ☐ use placement of adjectives. ☐ use participial adjectives, and make comparisons with *less* and *least*.
Writing	☐ write a book review. ☐ write a persuasive paragraph. ☐ write a diary entry. ☐ write a critical evaluation. ☐ write a persuasive speech.

TEST 1

DIRECTIONS
Read this selection. Then answer the questions that follow it.

Helping Pets When Disaster Hits

1 When a disaster like Hurricane Katrina hits, many people have to leave their pets behind. This is always a difficult decision. Pets are lonely and __1__ without their owners. Sometimes they are injured or killed when the disaster hits. Or, they may starve to death when they run out of food and water.

2 Even before Katrina hit, the ASPCA was on the scene trying to help. Many __2__ worked 20-hour days without pay rescuing pets that had been trapped or stranded by the floodwaters. They stayed long after the hurricane was over to help reunite families with their beloved pets and to find new homes for animals that were left homeless. In all, the ASPCA helped more than 8,000 pets.

1 **A** purebred
B playful
C frightened
D happy

2 **F** volunteers
G musicians
H celebrities
J prisoners

3 In paragraph 1, hurricane means —
A a dangerous tornado
B a type of earthquake
C a large tropical storm
D a major winter storm

TEST 2

DIRECTIONS

Read this selection. Then answer the questions that follow it.

Bark Park

1 Many groups across the country work to help animals. They find money to help buy food, and they find homes for unwanted animals. Some of these groups even find areas in cities to build dog parks.

2 There are now 1,100 successful dog parks in the United States and Canada. The dog parks are special areas inside existing parks. These are parks that cities have already built for people. The dog parks are surrounded with fences. The fences give dogs a spot to play without wearing a leash. The dogs get exercise and a chance to play with other dogs. Dog owners also appreciate getting a chance to meet and visit with other dog owners. They can make new friends as their pets play.

3 Large and small cities in the United States and Canada are interested in building dog parks. Building the parks is not expensive. For very little money, cities can help dogs and their owners enjoy the outdoors. Cities with dog parks are the best cities for people with pets to live in.

1 What is paragraph 2 mainly about?

- **A** Dog parks and why people and dogs like them
- **B** How important it is for dogs to get enough exercise
- **C** What dog parks look like
- **D** How cities build dog parks

2 Which sentence in paragraph 3 is an opinion?

- **F** *Large and small cities in the United States and Canada are interested in building dog parks.*
- **G** *Building the parks is not expensive.*
- **H** *Cities with dog parks are the best cities for people with pets to live in.*
- **J** *For very little money, cities can help dogs and their owners enjoy the outdoors.*

3 In paragraph 2, what words help the reader know what *existing* means?

- **A** surrounded with
- **B** have already built
- **C** a spot to play
- **D** special areas

4 Why are cities interested in building dog parks?

- **F** It is not expensive.
- **G** They need to find homes for unwanted animals.
- **H** They need to raise money to help feed unwanted dogs.
- **J** Cities can help dogs and their owners enjoy the outdoors.

Name ______________________________ Date ______________

TEST 3

DIRECTIONS
Read this selection. Then answer the questions that follow it.

Stone Soup

1 A long, long time ago, there was a great famine in many villages. There was not enough food, and villagers hid from each other what food they could find. One day, a stranger came to a village. The people in the village looked at him distrustfully as he walked toward the town square. An old man called out, "There's no food here! Best to keep walking!"

2 "I don't need your food," the stranger replied, "I have brought my own. And if you could bring me a large pot of water and some firewood, I'll share some with you." The old man hurried into his house and came out with a pot full of water and some wood.

3 As the stranger built a fire and began to boil the water, a crowd gathered around him. The stranger took from his pocket a small stone and said, "I am going to make some soup with this magic stone. It's the best soup you'll ever taste!" Then he put the stone into the water.

4 Tasting a bit of the water, he said. "This is good, but soup needs salt. Can someone get some?" A woman ran to her house and brought him some salt. "And does anyone have any onions? Stone soup is so much better with onions." And so another villager brought him four big, juicy onions. The stranger continued to ask for more things for the soup—cabbage, celery, chicken, pork, and sausage—which the hungry people cheerfully brought.

5 When the soup was ready, the stranger shared the soup with all the people in the town square. Everyone agreed it was the best soup they had ever tasted and thanked the stranger for sharing it. Once the pot was empty, the stranger removed the stone and put it back into his pocket. He asked for directions to the next village and said goodbye to the happy people.

1 What is the villagers' main problem?

A They do not have enough food.
B They cannot find enough wood for the soup.
C The stranger needed to add salt to the soup.
D They did not trust the stranger.

2 Paragraph 4 is mainly about —

F adding onions to the soup
G how the villagers find food to make the soup
H how the villagers find salt to add to the soup
J the recipe the stranger uses to make the soup

3 In paragraph 1, what words help the reader know what *famine* means?

A hid from each other
B many villages
C food they could find
D not enough food

4 The reader can conclude that the stranger wanted to —

F teach the villagers how to build a fire
G teach the villagers to share with each other
H teach the villagers how to find a magic stone
J teach the villagers how to make soup

5 Which sentence in paragraph 5 shows what the stranger is going to do next?

A *When the soup was ready, the stranger shared the soup with all the people in the town square.*
B *Once the pot was empty, the stranger removed the stone and put it back into his pocket.*
C *He asked for directions to the next village and said goodbye to the happy people.*
D *Everyone agreed it was the best soup they had ever tasted and thanked the stranger for sharing it.*

Name ______________________________ Date ______________

Visual Literacy: Smithsonian American Art Museum *Use with textbook pages 224–225.*

LEARNING TO LOOK

Look at *Mis Hermanos* by Jesse Treviño on page 224 in your textbook. Use a blank piece of paper to cover all of the men in the painting except the man on the far right, who is sitting on the fence and holding a glass. Write down four observations about the man on the far right who is holding a glass. State facts, not opinions.

Example: *He wears a watch on his right wrist.*

1. ______________________________
2. ______________________________
3. ______________________________
4. ______________________________

INTERPRETATION

Look at *Mis Hermanos* by Jesse Treviño again. Imagine that someone else joins the men in this painting.

Where should he or she be positioned in the painting?

Example: *He should be sitting on the fence on the right side.*

____

____

What should he or she wear?

____

____

Draw a simple sketch of the new person you would add to the painting.

COMPARE & CONTRAST

Look at *Mis Hermanos* by Jesse Treviño again and *"Men exist for the sake of one another . . ."* by Jacob Lawrence on page 225 in your textbook. Write down three differences you see between the two artworks in the chart. Then write three similarities between them in the chart.

Jesse Treviño ***Mis Hermanos***	**Jacob Lawrence** ***"Men exist for the sake of one another . . ."***
Differences	
The men all have dark hair on their heads.	*The man has light hair on his head.*
1.	
2.	
3.	
Similarities	
4.	
5.	
6.	

Name ______________________________ Date ______________

What do we learn through winning and losing?

READING 1: "Casey at the Bat" / "Swift Things Are Beautiful" / "Buffalo Dusk"

VOCABULARY **Literary Words** *Use with textbook page 229.*

REMEMBER Poetry often uses patterns to create effects. The regular, repeated pattern of sounds is called **rhythm**. Repeating the same sound is **repetition**. The pattern made by words that end with the same sound is the **rhyme scheme**.

Read each sentence in the chart. Underline the words you stress as you read. Then check the box to show if the sentence uses rhyme, rhythm, or repetition.

Sentence	Rhythm	Repetition	Rhyme
Don't be <u>late</u>, <u>Nate</u>, for our <u>skate</u>.			✔
1. We will run, run, run down the road.			
2. Will they stay, or go away, and come back another day?			
3. Look left, look right, look left again.			
4. I say I do not hope, but I do hope, I hope with all my heart.			
5. Our faces will glow as we race through the snow.			

Read the nursery rhyme "Humpty Dumpty." Circle examples of repetition. Underline the words that rhyme. Then use the letters *a, b,* and *c* to label the rhyme scheme.

Humpty Dumpty

Example: (Humpty Dumpty) sat on a <u>wall</u>. *a*

6. Humpty Dumpty had a great fall. ______
7. All the king's horses ______
8. And all the king's men ______
9. Couldn't put Humpty together again ______

10. Does this poem have rhythm? __________

VOCABULARY **Academic Words** *Use with textbook page 230.*

Read the paragraph below. Pay attention to the underlined academic words.

The poem "Casey at the Bat" is about a baseball game. It is thirteen stanzas long, so it is not a brief poem. Each stanza has a definite structure—each is four lines long. Every two lines rhyme with each other, and this poetic device helps create rhythm. The poet describes the game using colorful language. For example, he calls a baseball a "leather-covered sphere." He captures the spirit of the fans as they loudly respond to the game. The suspense builds as the game goes on, so that the reader really wonders what is going to happen in the final stanza.

Write the letter of the correct definition next to each word.

Example: ___c___ brief

_______ **1.** device

_______ **2.** final

_______ **3.** respond

_______ **4.** sphere

_______ **5.** structure

a. last in a series of actions or events

b. the way parts connect to form a whole

c. continuing for a short time

d. something in the shape of a ball

e. react to something that has been said or done

f. a way of achieving a particular purpose

Use the academic words from the exercise above to complete the sentences.

6. An orange is an example of a ____________________.

7. He asked a question and waited for me to ____________________.

8. Honeycombs have a ____________________ of six-sided cells.

Complete the sentences with your own ideas.

Example: One example of a literary device is *alliteration, or words that start with the same sound.*

9. When my homework takes a brief amount of time, I ____________________.

10. The final thing I do at the end of each day is ____________________.

Name ______________________________ Date ______________

WORD STUDY Spelling Long Vowel Sound /ī/

Use with textbook page 231.

REMEMBER The long /ī/ can be spelled in many ways, including *i* as in *grind*, *i_e* as in *spike*, *y* as in *fry*, *igh* as in *bright*, and *ie* as in *lie*. Knowing these patterns can help you spell and say many words with the long /ī/ correctly.

Read the words in the box below. Then write each word in the correct column in the chart.

~~pint~~	fried	flight	fly	bike
type	precise	denied	why	delight
behind	pie	find	bribe	night

/ī/ spelled *i*	/ī/ spelled *i_e*	/ī/ spelled *y*	/ī/ spelled *igh*	/ī/ spelled *ie*
pint				

Write the correct spelling pattern for /ī/ in each word below.

Example: bride /ī/ spelled i_e

1. mind ______________________
2. dry ______________________
3. might ______________________
4. tied ______________________
5. divide ______________________
6. sign ______________________

READING STRATEGY READ FOR ENJOYMENT

Use with textbook page 231.

REMEMBER When you read for enjoyment, you aren't just reading for information. You are reading to be entertained by other things, such as the characters, the setting, or the words.

Read and answer the questions below.

1. What is your favorite book?

____

2. What made the book so enjoyable?

____

____

____

3. What is the name of your all-time favorite character in a book?

____

4. What did you like best about that character?

____

____

____

5. Which kinds of texts do you most enjoy reading? Why?

____

____

____

____

____

____

____

Name ______________________________ Date ______________

COMPREHENSION

Use with textbook page 238.

Choose the best answer for each item. Circle the letter of the correct answer.

1. Why does the narrator say that the outlook wasn't brilliant for the Mudville team?

a. one of the players died during the game **b.** they were losing **c.** they were winning

2. The team's fans want ______.

a. the game to go into overtime **b.** Flynn to get up to bat **c.** Casey to get up to bat

3. At the end of "Casey at the Bat," the people in the town are sad because ______.

a. Casey did not get to play **b.** Casey hit a home run **c.** Casey struck out

4. In the poem "Swift Things Are Beautiful," the swift things named include ______.

a. lightning and wind **b.** cats and waterfalls **c.** skaters and swimmers

5. In "Buffalo Dusk," the poet describes buffaloes on the ______.

a. mountains **b.** prairie **c.** seashore

RESPONSE TO LITERATURE

Use with textbook page 239.

In this section you read three poems: "Casey at the Bat," "Swift Things Are Beautiful," and "Buffalo Dusk." Research to find another poem that you like. Copy the poem in the space below. Remember to include the title of the poem and the name of the poet.

GRAMMAR Present Perfect *Use with textbook page 240.*

REMEMBER Use the present perfect for actions that happened in the past but not at a specific time. Form the present perfect with *has* or *have* and the past participle. For the negative, use *hasn't* or *haven't*. For questions, switch *has* or *have* and the subject. For regular past participles, add *-d* or *-ed* to the base form of the verb. Other past participles are irregular.

Complete the chart with the past participles of the verbs in the box.

watch be sing go like talk buy take eat see write walk start work

Regular past participles	Irregular past participles

Complete each sentence with the verb in parentheses. Use the present perfect.

1. She ____________________ the baseball team. (join)
2. We ____________________ two games. (play)
3. I ____________________ any home runs. (not hit)
4. He ____________________ any games. (win)
5. ____________________ baseball? (you, play)
6. The pitcher ____________________ a no-hitter. (throw)

Name ______________________________ Date ______________

More Uses of the Present Perfect *Use with textbook page 241.*

REMEMBER You can use the prepositions *for* and *since* with the present perfect to show that an action began in the past and continues into the present.
Example: I have lived here for three years / since 2009.
Certain adverbs such as *just*, *yet*, *already*, and *ever* can be used with the present perfect to indicate general times.
Example: I have just finished lunch.

Write the phrases from the box in the correct place in the chart.

three years	2010	Monday	a week	five days	September

for	since

Choose the correct word to complete each sentence below.

1. He hasn't played soccer (already / yet).
2. We have (never / yet) been to France.
3. I've studied music (for / since) three years.
4. Bill has (never / ever) been absent before.
5. We have seen that movie three times (already / yet).
6. Haven't you finished your homework (yet / ever)?

Answer the questions with true information about you.

7. How long have you been in this class? ______________________________
8. How long have you studied ______________ (a subject)? ______________________________
9. How long have you played ______________ (a sport)? ______________________________

WRITING Write a Response to Literature *Use with textbook pages 242–243.*

Complete your own word web for a response to the poem "Casey at the Bat."

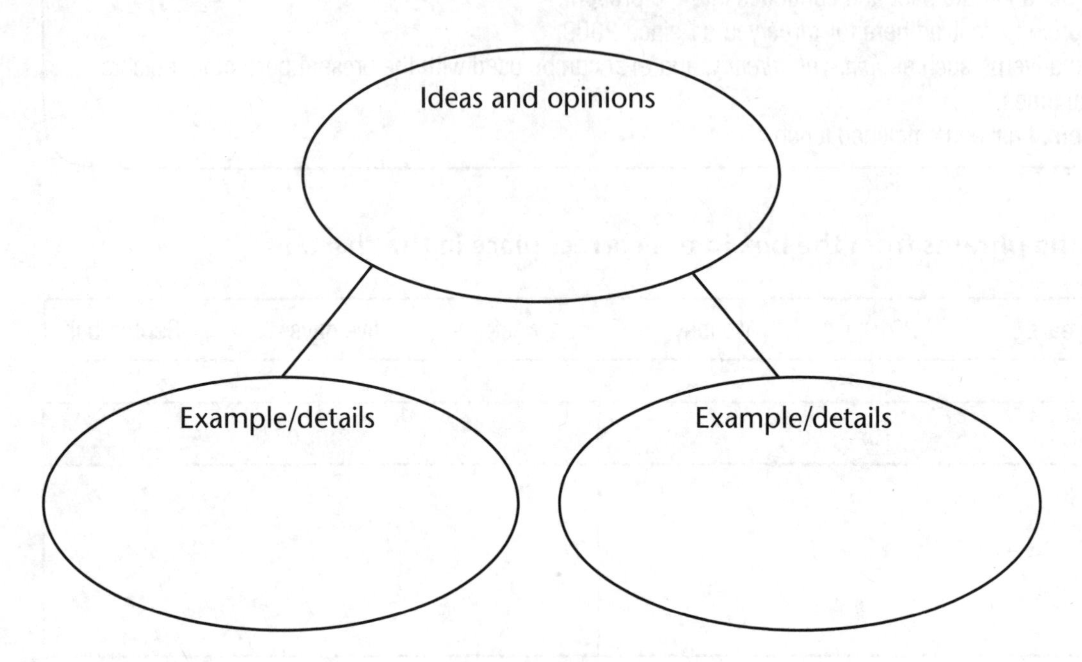

Use the Peer Review Checklist below to obtain feedback from your partner. This feedback will help you edit your final draft.

PEER REVIEW CHECKLIST

- ☐ Does the writer present a response to the assigned poem?
- ☐ Does the response include ideas about the poem's meaning?
- ☐ Do specific examples support the writer's ideas and opinions?
- ☐ Is the present perfect used correctly?
- ☐ Is each word spelled correctly?
- ☐ What changes could be made to improve the response to literature?

Name ______________________ Date ____________

What do we learn through winning and losing?

READING 2: "Going, Going, Gone?" / "Ivory-Billed Woodpeckers Make Noise"

VOCABULARY **Key Words** *Use with textbook page 245.*

Write each word in the box next to its definition.

conservationists	destruction	extinct	habitats	ornithology	predator

Example: ornithology: the study of birds

1. ____________: people who work to save natural things
2. ____________: the process of destroying something
3. ____________: places where plants or animals naturally live
4. ____________: an animal that kills and eats other animals
5. ____________: no longer existing

Use the words in the box at the top of the page to complete the sentences.

6. The ____________ of forests and marshes harms many animals.
7. The hawk is a ____________ that hunts birds and small animals.
8. Dinosaurs have been ____________ for thousands of years.
9. Some animals can only survive in very specific ____________.
10. ____________ work to make people understand the dangers of pollution.

VOCABULARY **Academic Words** *Use with textbook page 246.*

Read the paragraph below. Pay attention to the underlined academic words.

> Many plants and animals are disappearing from our planet. Statistics show that about 11,000 animals and plants are nearing total extinction. Scientists can only estimate how many more species are endangered. Climate change, pollution, and disease are some of the factors that can lead a species to disappear. Taking care of the environment is one way people can help save plants and animals from extinction.

Write the letter of the correct definition next to each word.

Example: __c__ environment

_____ **1.** estimate

_____ **2.** factors

_____ **3.** statistics

a. a collection of numbers that represents facts or measurements

b. several things that influence or cause a situation

c. the land, water, and air in which people, animals, and plants live

d. judge the value or size of something

Use the academic words from the exercise above to above complete the sentences.

4. You can ________________ how many jellybeans are in the jar.

5. Many different ________________ led to the team's success.

6. Some plants need a lot of water, but some can live in a dry ________________.

7. They tried to memorize the ________________ for each player on the other team.

Complete the sentences with your own ideas.

Example: The environment where penguins live is __very cold__.

8. Some factors that can affect my decisions are ________________.

9. To estimate the size of my room, I should ________________.

10. I use statistics to ________________.

Name ______________________ Date ____________

WORD STUDY **Homophones** *Use with textbook page 247.*

REMEMBER Homophones are words that sound the same but have different meanings and spellings. For example, *tern* and *turn* are homophones. A *ring* is a circle; *wring* means "to twist." To decide which homophone to use, first see how the word is spelled. If you are still confused, use a dictionary.

Write the definitions for each pair of homophones in the chart. Use a dictionary if needed.

Words	Definitions
guest; guessed	*visitor; supposed*
1. hall; haul	
2. racquet; racket	
3. flour; flower	
4. gorilla; guerilla	
5. heard; herd	

Write the definitions for each pair of homophones. Then use the words in one or two sentences that show their meaning.

Example: heel; heal *back part of the foot; cure*

The cut on her heel will heal in a week.

6. aunt; ant ______________________

____

7. they're; their ______________________

____

8. threw; through ______________________

____

9. Jim; gym ______________________

____

10. sail; sale ______________________

____

READING STRATEGY | RECOGNIZE CAUSE AND EFFECT

Use with textbook page 247.

REMEMBER When you recognize cause and effect, you understand the effect (what happened) and the cause (why it happened). Look for events, reasons, and clue words such as *so, because, because of, therefore,* and *as a result.*

Read each passage. Then answer the questions that follow.

"Here—you can have the last piece of pie," said Omar.
"But you love pumpkin pie," said Reem. "Why are you being so nice?"
"I just appreciate having a nice big sister like you."
"There has to be more than that."
"Well, okay. I accidentally knocked your tennis trophies off the shelf and broke one."

1. What was the cause in this passage?

____

2. What was the effect in this passage?

____

"I've got it!" said Professor Okumbo. She swirled the test tube and looked at the blue liquid in it. "From now on, no one will ever get sneezes, sniffles, or watery eyes. I've cured the common cold!" Pretty soon, Dr. Okumbo's cold fighting syrup was sold in drugstores all over the country. As a result, she became rich. Nobody ever suffered from a cold again.

3. What was the cause in this passage?

____

4. What were the effects in this passage?

____

5. How can the strategy of recognizing causes and effects help you to understand what you read better?

____

Name ______________________________ Date ______________

COMPREHENSION

Use with textbook page 252.

Choose the best answer for each item. Circle the letter of the correct answer.

1. "Going, Going, Gone?" says that the main cause of bird species becoming extinct is ______.

   a. disease **b.** natural disasters **c.** humans

2. In "Going, Going, Gone?" bird experts were excited by a possible sighting of ______.

   a. three passenger pigeons **b.** a Carolina parakeet **c.** an ivory-billed woodpecker

3. In modern times, the first bird wiped out by humans was ______.

   a. the Carolina parakeet **b.** the dodo **c.** the passenger pigeon

4. The only parrot native to the eastern United States was the ______.

   a. passenger pigeon **b.** ivory-billed woodpecker **c.** Carolina parakeet

5. Conservationists in Arkansas are trying to ______.

   a. help woodpeckers **b.** kill woodpeckers **c.** stop tree-cutting

EXTENSION

Use with textbook page 253.

The reading "Going, Going, Gone?" talks about bird species that are in danger or have become extinct. Birds aren't the only animals that are in danger. Research five more animals that are in danger or have already become extinct. Use the information you find to complete the table below.

Animal	Habitat	At Risk Because . . .
Giant Panda	*high, cold forests in China*	*hunting by humans; habitat being destroyed by humans*

GRAMMAR Complex Sentences with Subordinating Conjunctions

Use with textbook page 254.

REMEMBER A complex sentence has a main clause and one or more subordinate clauses. A subordinating conjunction, such as *when*, joins a subordinate clause to a main clause. A subordinate clause can come before or after the main clause. If it comes before the main clause, use a comma after the subordinate clause.
Example: When I called his name, the boy ran away.

Rewrite the sentences as complex sentences.

1. We stopped playing. It started to rain.

   ______________________ when ______________________

2. I saw the spider. I screamed.

   When ____

3. The birds flew away. They cut down the trees.

   ______________________ when ______________________

4. The birds ate the crops. The farmers got mad.

   When ____

Match the sentence parts.

5. When I went to the mall, ______ I went to bed.
6. I felt nervous ______ I bought a gift for my Mom.
7. When I finished my homework, ______ when I got home yesterday.
8. I called my friend ______ when I took the test last week.

Name ______________________________ Date ______________

Subordinating Conjunctions with Adverb Clauses *Use with textbook page 255.*

REMEMBER A subordinating conjunction introduces a subordinate clause. Often the subordinate clause is an adverb clause. An adverb clause answers the questions *Why? When?* or *How?* Examples of subordinating conjunctions are: *although, because, while, if, after, before.*

Rewrite each sentence as a complex sentence. Use correct punctuation.

1. He wasn't rich. He was happy.

Although ______________________________

2. He studied hard. He got good grades.

Because ______________________________

3. Read the instructions. You start the test.

______________ before ______________

4. I watched TV. I ate a sandwich.

While ______________________________

5. You should ask the teacher. You have a problem.

______________ if ______________

Complete each sentence with your own ideas.

6. Although I was busy, ______________________________.

7. ______________________________ because I was tired.

8. ______________________________ before I went to school.

9. After I came home from school, ______________________________.

10. While I did my homework, ______________________________.

WRITING Write a Cause-and-Effect Paragraph

Use with textbook pages 256–257.

Complete your own cause-and-effect chart for a paragraph that gives reasons why the ivory-billed woodpecker was nearly wiped out.

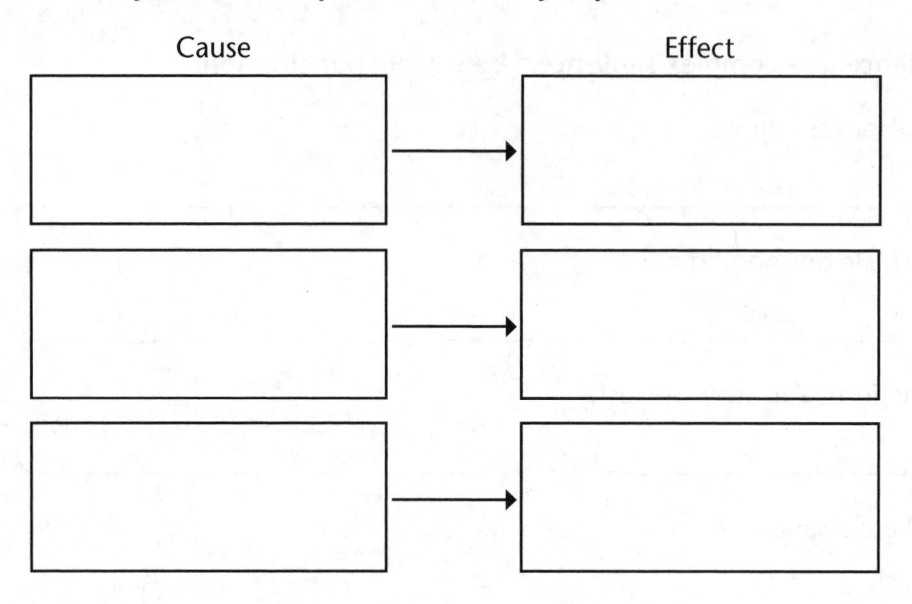

Use the Peer Review Checklist below to obtain feedback from your partner. This feedback will help you edit your final draft.

PEER REVIEW CHECKLIST

- ☐ Does the paragraph focus on the ivory-billed woodpecker?
- ☐ Is a cause-and-effect relationship explained?
- ☐ Is information presented in an order that makes sense?
- ☐ Do words such as *because* and *therefore* signal cause and effect?
- ☐ Are content-based words used accurately?
- ☐ What changes could be made to improve the paragraph?

Name ______________________________ Date ____________

What do we learn through winning and losing?

READING 3: "The Hare and the Tortoise" / "Orpheus and Eurydice"

VOCABULARY **Literary Words** *Use with textbook page 259.*

REMEMBER A **fable** is a short story that has a **moral**, or lesson. Fables often include **personification**, or animal characters that talk and act like human beings. A **myth** is a story from long ago; myths often try to explain events in nature, such as the seasons of the year.

Label each description as myth, fable, moral, or personification.

Description	Myth, Fable, Moral, or Personification?
A story that explains the origin of the seasons of the year	myth
1. Don't count your chickens before they've hatched.	
2. A story about an ant and a grasshopper that teaches a lesson	
3. A grateful lion	

Read the following story. Then answer the questions that follow.

A crow was very thirsty. When he saw a jug of water in a garden, he leaned in to take a drink. He soon realized that the jug was too narrow. Finally, he had an idea. He picked up pebbles with his beak and dropped them into the jug. Soon, the water rose higher. At last, the thirsty crow was able to drink. This shows that necessity is the mother of invention.

4. Is this story a fable or a myth? ____________

5. What is one example of an animal behaving like a human being in the story?

____

____

VOCABULARY **Academic Words** *Use with textbook page 260.*

Read the paragraph below. Pay attention to the underlined academic words.

Our teacher said she would instruct the class on how to make a glossary. Her objective, she said, was for us to learn the new vocabulary terms. She told us to define each vocabulary word and write a sentence including it. Then she asked us to draw a picture that would help us remember each word. She said the picture could be in any style we wanted—simple, complicated, or even comical. I think the glossary is a great idea.

Write the academic words from the paragraph above next to their correct definitions.

Example: ___style___: a way of doing, making, or painting something that is typical of a particular period

1. ________________: teach someone or show him or her how to do something
2. ________________: something that you are working hard to achieve
3. ________________: show or describe what something is or means

Use academic words from the paragraph above to complete the sentences.

4. My favorite ________________ of painting is Impressionism, which was popular in the late 1800s.
5. You need to understand something very well to ________________ someone else on the subject.
6. Sometimes you can use clues in a sentence to ________________ a word you don't know.
7. It helps to have a clear ________________ before starting something.

Complete the sentences with your own ideas.

Example: It can be easier to define a word if ___it is similar to another word you know___.

8. I could instruct someone to ________________________.
9. My style of writing is ________________________.
10. My objective for school this year is ________________________.

Name ______________________________ Date ______________

WORD STUDY **Spellings for *r*-Controlled Vowels**

Use with textbook page 261.

REMEMBER When *r* comes after a vowel, the vowel stands for a special sound–the *r*-controlled vowel. The *r*-controlled vowel sound can be spelled *ar* as in *far*, *er* as in *stern*, *ir* as in *bird*, *or* as in *orchard*, and *ur* as in *burn*.

Read the words in the box below. Then write each word in the correct column in the chart.

~~chart~~	force	thirst	father	fur
part	horn	turf	fern	stir

/är/ as in *bar*	/ər/ as in *concern*	/ər/ as in *flirt*	/ôr/ as in *nor*	/ər/ as in *surf*
chart				

Write the *r*-controlled vowel in each below.

Example: hurt ___ur___

1. spark ______________
2. mother ______________
3. remorse ______________
4. sir ______________
5. embark ______________
6. forth ______________

READING STRATEGY IDENTIFY AUTHOR'S PURPOSE

Use with textbook page 261.

REMEMBER When you read, try to identify the author's purpose, or the reason the author wrote the text. The main purposes an author has to write are: to entertain, to inform, or to persuade.

Read each passage below. Then answer the questions that follow each passage.

Animal shelters are a great place to find a pet. My cousin Jack adopted a mutt he called Sparky from an animal shelter. Sparky was shy at first, but soon he got used to all the love and attention he got from Jack. Then, one night, a fire started in the basement. Jack was fast asleep, but Sparky barked and barked. When Jack still didn't get up Sparky gave his hand a gentle nip. Jack woke up. Sparky saved him!

1. What is the author's purpose for writing?

____

2. What clues in the text indicate the author's purpose for writing?

____

Do you feel tired and have low energy in the morning? There's something easy that can help. It's called breakfast. Breakfast will give you energy and make you feel healthy. You may not like eggs, oatmeal, or cereal for breakfast, but there are other healthy choices, too. You could have yogurt and fruit. You could have peanut butter on toast or a ham sandwich. You could even eat leftover pizza.

3. What is the author's purpose for writing?

____

4. How does the author show his or her purpose?

____

5. How can the strategy of identifying an author's purpose help you to understand a text better?

____

____

Name ______________________________ Date ______________

COMPREHENSION

Use with textbook page 266.

Choose the best answer for each item. Circle the letter of the correct answer.

1. In the story "The Hare and the Tortoise," Hare loses the race because he _____.

   a. falls asleep **b.** loses his way **c.** forgets about the race

2. The moral of "The Hare and the Tortoise" is "Slow and steady . . . " _____.

   a. always ready **b.** wins the race **c.** nice and easy

3. In "Orpheus and Eurydice," Orpheus is a _____.

   a. famous writer **b.** skilled carpenter **c.** talented musician

4. To rescue his wife, Orpheus travels to _____.

   a. the Underworld **b.** the Mediterranean Sea **c.** the top of Mount Olympus

5. Orpheus loses his wife again when he _____.

   a. fails to charm Hades **b.** breaks his lyre **c.** looks back too soon

RESPONSE TO LITERATURE

Use with textbook page 267.

The story "Orpheus and Eurydice" reflects the time when it was first told. Orpheus plays a lyre, and Eurydice dies when she is bitten by a snake. Imagine how a story like this might be told today. What kind of music might Orpheus play? How might Eurydice die? What would their names be? Use your imagination to complete the graphic organizer for a modern retelling of the story.

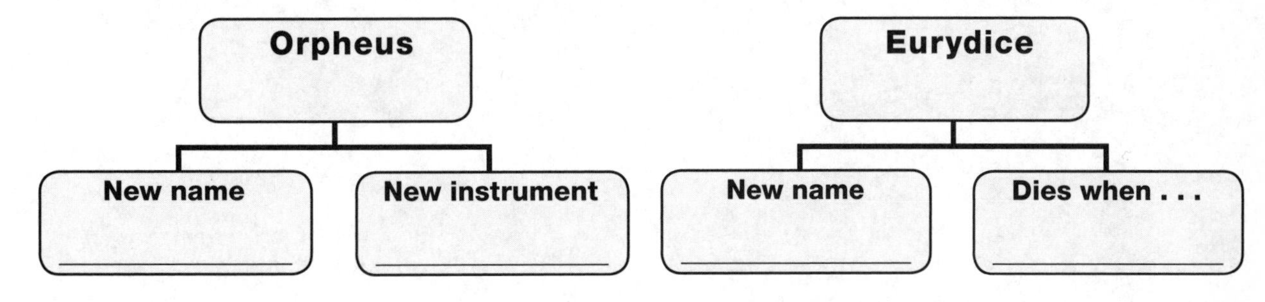

GRAMMAR **Adverbs of Manner** *Use with textbook page 268.*

REMEMBER An adverb describes a verb. Many adverbs answer the question *How*? These are called adverbs of manner. Form adverbs of manner by adding *-ly* to the adjective.
Example: *slow → slowly*

Complete the chart by forming an adverb from each adjective.

Adjective	Adverb
1. sad	
2. heavy	
3. final	
4. energetic	
5. terrible	

Write the correct verb form to complete each sentence.

6. The tortoise plodded ________________. (steady)

7. The hare started to walk ________________. (quick)

8. He jumped over rocks ________________. (easy)

9. Eurydice played music ________________. (beautiful)

10. She died ________________. (tragic)

11. Orpheus whispered to himself ________________. (hopeful)

12. He played the lyre ________________. (passionate)

Name ______________________ Date ____________

Placement of Adverbs of Manner *Use with textbook page 269.*

REMEMBER An adverb, unlike an adjective, can be in many places in a sentence. It can appear at the beginning, middle, or end of a sentence. It can go before or after a verb. Never put an adverb between the verb and the object.

Turn the adjectives in parentheses into adverbs. Then rewrite each sentence, inserting the adverbs where shown.

1. The lion crept ^ through the high grass. (soft)

   ____

2. We saw the wolf ^ in the moonlight. (clear)

   ____

3. The moon shone ^ in the night sky. (bright)

   ____

4. The lion ^ followed its prey. (careful)

   ____

5. The wolf howled ^ at the moon. (loud)

   ____

6. The rabbit had ^ won a race. (recent)

   ____

Write an adverb for each sentence.

7. ______________, she answered the phone.
8. They answered my questions ______________.
9. We walked ______________ to school.
10. I ______________ wrote down the answers.

WRITING Write a Compare-and-Contrast Paragraph

Use with textbook pages 270–271.

Complete your own Venn diagram for two paragraphs that compare and contrast two people, places, or things.

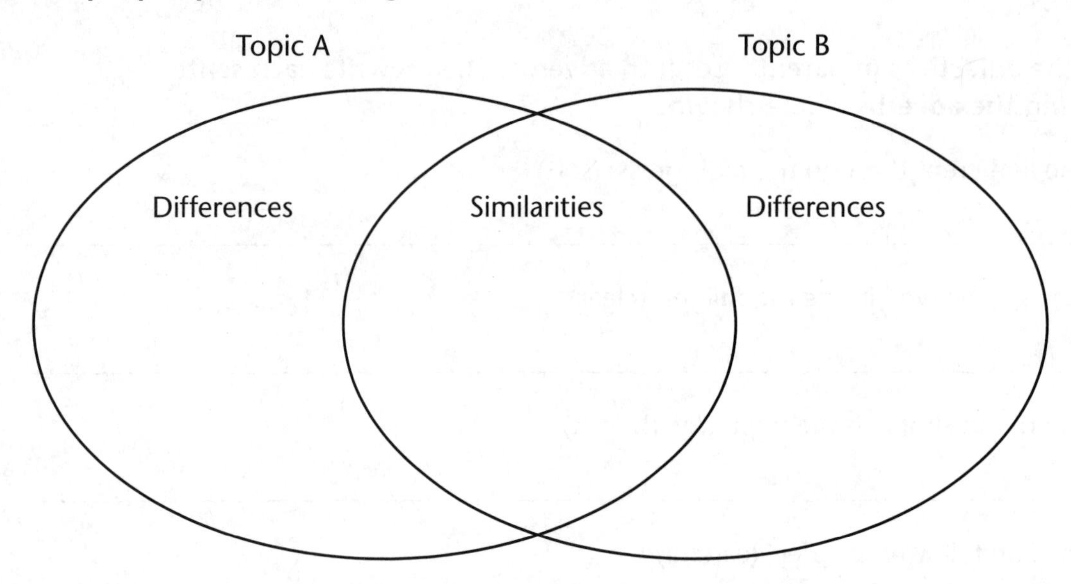

Use the Peer Review Checklist below to obtain feedback from your partner. This feedback will help you edit your final draft.

PEER REVIEW CHECKLIST

- ☐ Do the paragraphs compare and contrast two people or things?
- ☐ Are similarities presented in the first paragraph?
- ☐ Are differences presented in the second paragraph?
- ☐ Does the writer use signal words such as *also, too, although,* and *but?*
- ☐ Are adverbs of manner used correctly?
- ☐ What changes could be made to improve the paragraphs?

Name ______________________________ Date ______________

What do we learn through winning and losing?

READING 4: "The Biggest Winner of All"

VOCABULARY **Key Words** *Use with textbook page 273.*

Write each word in the box next to its definition.

cancer	chemotherapy	cycling	grueling	prestigious	triathlon

Example: *cancer*: a serious illness in which cells in one part of the body grow in a way that is not normal

1. ______________: a sports competition in which you run, swim, and ride a bicycle
2. ______________: the treatment of cancer using special medicine
3. ______________: admired or respected as one of the best and most important
4. ______________: the activity or sport of riding a bicycle
5. ______________: very difficult and tiring

Use the words in the box at the top of the page to complete the sentences.

6. I think that running is the hardest part of a ______________ because it comes last.
7. People who have ______________ should eat healthy food and get rest so they can feel stronger.
8. It was a ______________ five-hour climb to the top of the mountain.
9. He had very good grades, so he went to a ______________ college.
10. She doesn't like to go ______________ when it is very hot or very cold outside.

VOCABULARY **Academic Words** *Use with textbook page 274.*

Read the paragraph below. Pay attention to the underlined academic words.

The "Iditarod" is a famous, 1,161-mile dogsled race across Alaska. The cold weather and extreme length of the race require the racers and the dogs to be in their best physical shape. Good teamwork between man and dog is another important element of a successful dogsled team. The racers must focus on the dogs' performance and safety, and must project a positive attitude until the end. The event is considered one of the last great races of the world.

Write the academic words from the paragraph above next to their correct definitions.

Example: *require*: need something

1. ________________: good or useful
2. ________________: one part of a plan, system, piece of writing, and so on
3. ________________: give all your attention to a particular person or thing

Use the academic words from the paragraph above to complete the sentences.

4. All his hard work had a ________________ effect on his grades.
5. I know that if I ________________ on the problem, I can figure it out.
6. Sports like soccer ________________ a lot of practice.
7. Sports are an important ________________ of my life.

Complete the sentences with your own ideas.

Example: Having a positive approach *can help you do well at things*.

8. For me, sports and studying both require ________________.
9. This year I will focus on ________________.
10. The most interesting element of my current school project is ________________.

Name ______________________________ Date ______________

WORD STUDY Multiple-Meaning Words *Use with textbook page 275.*

REMEMBER Some words in English have more than one meaning. For example, as a noun, *bat* refers to an animal or baseball equipment. As a verb, it means "to hit." Use context clues, the word's part of speech or a dictionary to determine which meaning is being used.

Read each sentence. Identify the part of speech of each underlined word. Then define the word. Check your work with a dictionary.

Sentence	Part of Speech	Meaning
I need to go to the store.	*noun*	*a place that sells things*
1. We took a break from studying.		
2. The pencil will break if you play with it.		
3. The spring on the bed is loose.		
4. Spring is my favorite season of all.		
5. Tomorrow, I will spring out of bed and get my chores done!		

Look at the sentences in the chart below. Write the meanings and part of speech of each word in the chart. Use a dictionary if needed.

Multiple-Meaning Word	Part of speech/ Meaning	Part of speech/ Meaning
We roast marshmallows over the fire. The boss will fire them.	*noun: flames*	*verb: to remove from a job*
6. The rose smelled so sweet. I rose from my chair in excitement.		
7. Come to my place after school. Place the glass on the shelf, please.		
8. Gary pounds the post into the ground. The teacher will post the grades.		
9. We bought a tire for the truck. The kids tire me out.		

READING STRATEGY ASK QUESTIONS *Use with textbook page 275.*

REMEMBER When you read, it is important to check your understanding of the text you are reading. One good technique is to ask questions using the 5Ws: *Who? Where? When? What? Why?* Then try to answer the questions from what you've learned in the text.

Read the paragraph and answer the questions that follow.

Julio wanted to go to college. He studied hard. He went to an after-school math class because he found math difficult. At his high school outside El Paso, there are many athletic teams. Julio played on the football and track teams. After four years of hard work, Julio got into a great college.

1. Who is this passage about?

____

2. Where did this passage take place?

____

In 1872, my great-great grandparents left Italy. They travelled by boat to New York City. For many years, they struggled. My great-great grandfather worked as a lamplighter. My great-great grandmother worked as a maid. Life was hard.

3. Who is this passage about?

____

4. When do the events in this passage take place?

____

5. How do you think asking questions can help you to understand what you read better?

____

Name ______________________________ Date ______________

COMPREHENSION

Use with textbook page 280.

Choose the best answer for each item. Circle the letter of the correct answer.

1. The distance for each triathlon event depends on _______.

   a. age **b.** weight **c.** experience

2. Lance became a professional athlete by the time he _______.

   a. was 13 **b.** was 16 **c.** joined the U.S. Olympic team

3. For Lance, a cycling competition was _______ fighting cancer.

   a. the same as **b.** harder than **c.** easier than

4. Cyclists in the Tour de France ride _______.

   a. in mountains only **b.** on different types of land **c.** in cities in France only

5. Lance felt _______, which helped him beat cancer.

   a. happy and tired **b.** angry and nervous **c.** hopeful and confident

EXTENSION

Use with textbook page 281.

Lance Armstrong started a foundation that helps people with cancer. Write about Lance's foundation or another group you know about that helps people. Use the library or the Internet to do research if you need help finding information.

____

____

____

____

____

____

____

____

____

GRAMMAR **Past Perfect** *Use with textbook page 282.*

REMEMBER Use the past perfect to describe something that happened before a specific time in the past. Form the past perfect with *had* + the past participle. For regular past participles, add *-d* or *-ed* to the base form of the verb. Other past participles are irregular. For the negative, use *hadn't.* For questions, switch *had* and the subject.

Complete the sentences using the past perfect of the verbs in parentheses.

1. He ________________ a bicycle for many years. (ride)
2. By the time he was 16, he ________________ many competitions. (win)
3. He ________________ first place on the Olympic team before he learned he had cancer. (earn)
4. He ________________ a challenge as difficult as this. (face, never)
5. He ________________ up hope that he would overcome cancer. (give, never)

Complete the sentences with your own ideas.

6. By the time I was five years old, ________________________________.
7. ________________________________ before I started school.
8. Before I came to this school, ________________________________.
9. ________________________ before I started to study English grammar.

Name ______________________________ Date ______________

Past Perfect and Simple Past *Use with textbook page 283.*

> **REMEMBER** Use the past perfect and the simple past together to show two events that happened in the past. The clause in the past perfect shows the first action; the clause in the simple past shows the action that happened after that.
> **Example:** Before I entered the race, I had never won any competitions.

Complete the sentences. Use the past perfect or the simple past.

1. We __________________ (look) at many houses before we __________________ (choose) this one.
2. By the time I __________________ (be) twelve, I __________________ (go) to four different schools.
3. Before he __________________ (enter) the competition, he __________________ (train) for many months.
4. My sister __________________ (visit) several countries, before she __________________ (move) to Australia.
5. He __________________ (buy) a new car after he __________________ (pass) his driving test.

Match the parts of the sentences.

6. By the time I was three,	______ before I was eight.
7. I had learned to ride a bike	______ by the time the test finished.
8. I had never been in an airplane	______ I had never seen the ocean.
9. Before we went to California	______ I already knew how to read.
10. I had answered all the questions	______ before we flew to Florida.

WRITING **Write a Newspaper Article** *Use with textbook pages 284–285.*

Complete your own 5Ws chart for a newspaper article about a sports event or other competition or game that you found exciting.

Who?
Where?
When?
What?
Why?

Use the Peer Review Checklist below to obtain feedback from your partner. This feedback will help you edit your final draft.

PEER REVIEW CHECKLIST

- ☐ Does the article focus on a competition?
- ☐ Is the event an exciting one that will interest readers?
- ☐ Does the article answer the 5Ws?
- ☐ Does the writer show knowledge of the topic?
- ☐ Is the past perfect used correctly?
- ☐ What changes could be made to improve the article?

Name ______________________________ Date ______________

WRITING WORKSHOP

Use with textbook pages 290–293.

Organize your ideas in the graphic organizer below.

Cause	Effect

Use the Peer Review Checklist below to obtain feedback from your partner. This feedback will help you edit your final draft.

PEER REVIEW CHECKLIST

- ☐ Does the essay have an introduction and conclusion?
- ☐ Does it include precise words and specific examples and details?
- ☐ Does the order of information fit the topic?
- ☐ Does the writing have energy?
- ☐ Are adverbs of manner used correctly?
- ☐ What changes could be made to improve the essay?

LEARNING LOG *Use after completing page 294.*

Underline the vocabulary items you know and can use well. Review and practice any you haven't underlined. Underline them when you know them well.

Literary Words	Key Words	Academic Words	
rhythm	conservationists	brief	statistics
repetition	destruction	device	define
rhyme scheme	extinct	final	instruct
fable	habitats	respond	objective
moral	ornithology	sphere	style
personification	predator	structure	element
myth	cancer	environment	focus
	chemotherapy	estimate	positive
	cycling	factors	require
	grueling		
	prestigious		
	triathlon		

Put a check by the skills you can perform well. Review and practice any you haven't checked off. Check them off when you can perform them well.

Skills	I can . . .
Word Study	☐ recognize and spell words with the long vowel sound /ī/. ☐ recognize and spell homophones. ☐ recognize and spell *r*-controlled vowels. ☐ recognize words with multiple meanings.
Reading Strategies	☐ read for enjoyment. ☐ recognize cause and effect. ☐ identify the author's purpose. ☐ ask questions.
Grammar	☐ use the present perfect. ☐ use complex sentences with subordinating conjunctions and subordinating conjunctions with adverb clauses. ☐ use adverbs of manner. ☐ use the past perfect and simple past.
Writing	☐ write a response to literature. ☐ write to show cause and effect. ☐ write to compare and contrast. ☐ write a newspaper article. ☐ write an expository essay.

Test Preparation

TEST 1

DIRECTIONS
Read this selection. Then answer the questions that follow it.

The Watchful Hikers

1 One day two friends decided to hike along the Tejas Trail in Dog Canyon. Juan packed water and food. Pete carried their map and other equipment. The experienced hikers checked in at the trailhead, then set off in the early light.

2 The sun sparkled through the large maples and pines that grew along the well-worn trail. Years of use had made the pathway easy to follow. The men moved along at an easy pace, careful not to step on the bluebells and cardinal flowers that grew on the forest floor. They were also on the lookout for the black-tailed rattlesnake, a beautiful but deadly critter commonly seen in the park.

3 As they came to a bend in the trail, Pete spotted three huge rocks. "This is a perfect spot to have lunch and rest our feet," he said.

4 Suddenly, Juan heard a sound near the rocks. All at once, the biggest boulder moved! It wasn't a rock at all, but a large black bear! Fortunately, the bear was just as startled as the hikers were. She took off into the bushes just as Juan and Pete ran back down the trail toward home.

1 In paragraph 2, well-worn means —

A much appreciated
B nicely trimmed
C full of weeds
D much used

2 The hikers ran away from ______.

F a deadly rattlesnake
G a black bear
H sore feet
J a bend in the trail

TEST 2

DIRECTIONS
Read this selection. Then answer the questions that follow it.

Dian Fossey

1 Dian Fossey was a scientist. She studied mountain gorillas in Africa. She wanted to learn about them. She wanted to find the answers to her questions: How many gorillas were there? What did they eat? How did they live together?

2 Fossey watched the gorillas for many years. She used maps and followed different groups of gorillas. She watched them carefully. She wrote down what they did. She tried to get close to them. She was not afraid, even though a male mountain gorilla can weigh more than 340 pounds.

3 Over the years, Fossey was able to get close to the gorillas. She learned some of the answers to her questions, but not all of them. For example, she learned that there were only 250 mountain gorillas. She saw that they lived in large families and were gentle. She learned that the gorillas ate mostly plants. Even though she did not answer all of her questions, she did not stop studying the gorillas.

1 Paragraph 2 is mainly about —

A how Fossey studied the gorillas
B the questions Fossey wanted to answer
C how Fossey remembered the answers she found
D how Fossey felt while she studied the gorillas

2 The selection is best described as —

F informative
G humorous
H persuasive
J expressive

3 What does Fossey use to follow different groups of mountain gorillas?

A compass
B computer
C radio
D maps

4 Which sentence in paragraph 3 answers Fossey's question "How did they live together?"

F *She saw they lived in large families and were gentle.*
G *She learned the gorillas ate mostly plants.*
H *Over the years, Fossey was able to get close to the gorillas.*
J *For example, she learned that there were only 250 mountain gorillas.*

Name ______________________________ Date ______________

TEST 3

DIRECTIONS
Read this selection. Then answer the questions that follow it.

Sports: Good or Bad?

1 Should sports teams be part of Callaway schools? Two groups of people have different opinions about this question. Parents for Sports is a group of parents who feel that sports teams in schools helps students. Say No to Sports is a group of parents who feel that sports teams in schools are harmful to students.

2 Parents for Sports believes that sports teams in schools help students learn important lessons. They think that team members learn ways of thinking that will help them in their classes and in their other activities. They also think that students learn skills that they can use for the rest of their lives. This group feels that competing in sports helps students learn confidence, or a belief in themselves. They feel that playing sports in schools teaches important lessons and brings students together.

3 Say No to Sports is a group of parents that believe sports teams in schools harm students. First, they think school sports programs take time away from classes and schoolwork. They feel that lessons learned in the classroom are more important than lessons learned through playing sports. They feel that students should spend their time after school helping at home and doing homework. The group also feels that playing sports puts students into two groups—winners and losers. They feel that if students lose when playing sports they will lose confidence and not do well in other activities.

4 Even though these two groups do no not agree about sports programs in school, they do agree that the happiness of students is most important. Both groups are meeting at the Calloway Community Center this Monday to discuss the issue. Everyone is invited to attend.

1 Look at this graphic organizer.

Parents for Sports	Say No to Sports
Students learn ways of thinking that help them in their classes.	Sports programs take time away from schoolwork.
Students learn skills they can use for the rest of their lives.	
Students learn to believe in themselves.	Students lose confidence if they lose.

Look at this chart about the opinions of the two groups. Which opinion best completes the chart?

A Students learn that nobody wins all of the time.
B Students should spend their time helping and doing homework.
C Sports brings students together.
D Student happiness is most important.

2 Paragraph 2 is mainly about —

F the beliefs of Parents for Sports
G the meeting between the two groups
H the beliefs of Say No to Sports
J how students learn from sports teams

3 In paragraph 2, what words help the reader know what *confidence* means?

A reach one goal
B learn to work
C competing in sports
D belief in themselves

4 According to the article, what is one thing that the groups agree on?

F Sports programs are an important part of Calloway schools.
G Sports programs teach students that winning is better than losing.
H Students should spend their time doing schoolwork.
J The most important thing is that students are happy.

5 The author wrote this selection to —

A inform readers about the opinions of the two groups
B express an opinion about the two groups
C make readers laugh
D explain how schools start sports programs

Name ______________________ Date ____________

Visual Literacy: Smithsonian American Art Museum *Use with textbook pages 296–297.*

LEARNING TO LOOK

Look at *Baseball at Night* by Morris Kantor on page 297 in your textbook. How many shapes can you find in the painting? List them below.

Example: *The pitcher stands in a circle.*

____

____

____

____

INTERPRETATION

Look at *Rejects from the Bat Factory* by Mark Sfirri on page 296 of your textbook. The artist created five different bat shapes out of five different woods. Which is your favorite? Why?

____

____

If you could add a bat to this work of art what would it look like? Sketch it below.

What material would it be made from?

____

____

Where would you place it? Why?

____

____

5W&H

Look at *Baseball at Night* again. Imagine you could interview a fan in the stands. What would you ask him or her? Use *Who, Where, When, What, Why* and *How* to frame your questions.

Example: How *often do you come to the night games?*

1. **Who** ______________________________

____

2. **Where** ______________________________

____

3. **When** ______________________________

____

4. **What** ______________________________

____

5. **Why** ______________________________

____

6. **How** ______________________________

____

Name ________________________________ Date ______________

How are courage and imagination linked?

READING 1: From *The Secret Garden*

VOCABULARY **Literary Words** *Use with textbook page 301.*

REMEMBER Playwrights start by **setting the scene**, or giving details about the time and place. The **list of characters** shows each person in the play. The **stage directions** tell actors how to look and act. Stage directions also tell about the scenery and costumes.

Read each passage. In the space provided, write *setting the scene* if the passage gives facts about the time and place. Write *character* if the passage describes a character. Write *stage directions* if the passage tells the actors and set designers what to do.

Literary Word	Example
character	Cynthia Jones, an Asian factory worker, age twenty
1.	Around 2005. A kitchen in a country house.
2.	Nick Jameson, an artist, age thirty-three
3.	[*Luis shakes Nita's hand while the lights dim.*]
4.	World War II. Chicago's Southside. Living room of a small apartment. Young child sleeping on the sofa.
5.	[*Nita exits the stage. A spotlight shines on a table in the center of the stage.*]

Read the passage from the play "Moving Day." Write *setting, character,* or *stage direction* in the circles. The first example is done.

Moving Day

Characters

Mama, strong woman but very tired — *character*

6. Noelle Richards, age 15

7. Present day. Living room of a big house. Lots of boxes stacked up.

Mama: [*Sighing and looking at her watch*] This is not going well. Not at all. **8.** **9.**

Noelle: [*Smiling at her mother*] How can I help?

Mama: [*Laughing*] I wish I knew! Look at this mess! **10.**

VOCABULARY Academic Words *Use with textbook page 302.*

Read the paragraph below. Pay attention to the underlined academic words.

My school is putting on the drama *Our Town* this year. The director is very good. He is teaching the actors how to convey emotion through voice, movement, and expression. He is working to make sure everyone on stage and behind the scenes will cooperate. He is also always very helpful when I approach him with a question or problem.

Write the academic words from the paragraph above next to their correct definitions.

Example: drama: a play for the theater, television, radio, and so forth

1. ________________: work with someone else to achieve something that you both want
2. ________________: communicate a message or information, with or without using words
3. ________________: move closer to someone or something

Use the academic words from the paragraph above to complete the sentences.

4. The ________________ was performed first on the stage and then on television.
5. Lisa and her parents ________________ to get their chores done faster.
6. You should never ________________ a strange dog; stay far away!
7. Actors ________________ feelings with their faces, voices, and body movements.

Complete the sentences with your own ideas.

Example: In our class drama, I'm hoping to get the lead part.

8. It is important to cooperate because ________________.
9. You should never approach a bear because ________________.
10. Dogs convey they are happy by ________________.

Name ______________________________ Date ______________

WORD STUDY **Spelling Words with *oo*** *Use with textbook page 303.*

REMEMBER The letters *oo* can stand for either the short sound /o͝o/ as in *look* or the long sound /o͞o/ as in *moose*. Knowing these sound spellings helps you spell and say many words correctly.

Read the words in the box below to yourself. Listen for the long or short sound of *oo*. Then write each word in the correct column in the chart.

~~rookie~~	school	brook	snooze	spoon
misunderstood	root	pocketbook	balloon	foot

Short Sound of *oo* as in *cook*	Long Sound of *oo* as in *shampoo*
rookie	

Read each word below to yourself, listening for the long or short sound of *oo*. Write *long oo* or *short oo* next to each word. Then think of a word that rhymes with each word and has the same sound spelling. Write the word and use the rhyming words in a sentence of your own.

Examples: monsoon *long oo balloon I lost my balloon during the monsoon.*

foot *short oo soot How did only one foot get covered with soot?*

1. pool ______________________________
2. scoot ______________________________
3. crook ______________________________
4. goose ______________________________
5. wood ______________________________

READING STRATEGY ANALYZE TEXT STRUCTURE 1

Use with textbook page 303.

REMEMBER Analyzing text structure helps you to understand what kind of text you are reading. Different kinds of writing have different kinds of text structure. For instance, stories are written in sentences and paragraphs, while poems are usually written in stanzas. Plays are made up mostly of dialogue.

Read each passage and answer the questions that follow.

A day in the sun
is a whole lot of fun
we skip and play
the lovely day away!

1. What are some features of the text above that show it is a poem?

____

____

2. What are some ways the text structure of a poem is different than the text structure of a story?

____

____

JAMIE: Did you do your homework?
JOHN: Yes. I always do my homework.
JAMIE: So do I.
JOHN: Great! Let's go and play.

3. What is the text structure of the passage above?

____

4. What features in the text helped you to understand that the text is a play?

____

____

5. How can the strategy of analyzing text structure help you to understand what you read?

____

Name ______________________________ Date ______________

COMPREHENSION

Use with textbook page 312.

Choose the best answer for each item. Circle the letter of the correct answer.

1. Dickon is not like most kids because he ______.

   a. talks to animals **b.** comes from India **c.** likes gardens

2. Mrs. Craven's favorite place was ______.

   a. her room **b.** the garden **c.** the big house

3. The children ______.

   a. ignore the garden **b.** dislike the garden **c.** fix the garden

4. The end of the play suggests that ______.

   a. Mr. Craven will be happier **b.** Colin will leave **c.** Mary will marry Dickon

5. This play shows the importance and power of ______.

   a. animals **b.** opening gardens to everyone **c.** friendship and love

RESPONSE TO LITERATURE

Use with textbook page 313.

Write a scene that tells what happens next in the play. Set the scene and use stage directions. Write at least five lines.

____

____

____

____

____

____

____

____

GRAMMAR ***Be going to* and *will*** *Use with textbook page 314.*

REMEMBER You can use *be going to* or *will* to make predictions about the future. To express a plan, use *be going to*. To show a decision made at the moment of speaking, use *will*.

Match each sentence with its meaning.

1. I'll tell you a secret.

a. prediction **b.** future plan **c.** a decision made at the time of speaking

2. I'm going to play in the garden.

a. prediction **b.** future plan **c.** a decision made at the time of speaking

3. We'll see you later.

a. prediction **b.** future plan **c.** a decision made at the time of speaking

4. You'll feel better tomorrow.

a. prediction **b.** future plan **c.** a decision made at the time of speaking

Are these sentences correct, or not? Correct the mistakes.

	Correct	Incorrect
5. They is going to live in England.	☐	☐
6. She'll make new friends.	☐	☐
7. They don't will like the food.	☐	☐
8. We're going look after the garden.	☐	☐
9. They're going to be friends.	☐	☐
10. He'll to get better.	☐	☐

Name ______________________________ Date ______________

Degrees of Certainty about the Future *Use with textbook page 315.*

REMEMBER When you are sure about the future, use *will* or *be going to.* When you are less certain, you can include the adverbs *probably, perhaps,* and *maybe.*
Example: Perhaps we'll go out tomorrow.
You can also use the modals *may* and *might* to express uncertainty. Use *may* or *might* with the base form of the verb. Form the negative of *may* and *might* with *not.*
Example: They might not come to the party tonight.

Rewrite these sentences using the modals *may* or *might.*

1. She is probably going to look for the secret garden.

____

2. Perhaps someone will give her the key.

____

3. Maybe Colin won't need a wheelchair any more.

____

Rewrite these sentences using the future and the adverbs in parentheses.

4. The children may play in the garden every day. (probably)

____

5. Mary might help Colin to get better. (perhaps)

____

6. Colin might not feel sad any more. (maybe)

____

Write the words in the correct order to make sentences.

7. soccer / we / might / play / this Saturday

____

8. this summer / not / they / go / may / to the beach

____

9. we / see / on Saturday / probably / to / a movie / are / going

____

WRITING Write a Formal E-mail *Use with textbook pages 316–317.*

Complete your own problem-solution chart for a formal e-mail to your community's mayor about a problem you want to solve in your neighborhood.

Problem	Solution

Use the Peer Review Checklist below to obtain feedback from your partner. This feedback will help you edit your final draft.

PEER REVIEW CHECKLIST

- ☐ Does the e-mail focus on a problem and solution?
- ☐ Is it addressed to the mayor of a community?
- ☐ Is a possible solution explained with specificity and detail?
- ☐ Does the language fit a formal e-mail?
- ☐ Are future verbs used correctly?
- ☐ What changes could be made to improve the letter?

Name ______________________________ Date ______________

How are courage and imagination linked?

READING 2: "A Tree Grows in Kenya: The Story of Wangari Maathai" / "How to Plant a Tree"

VOCABULARY **Key Words** *Use with textbook page 319.*

Write each word in the box next to its definition.

campaign	committee	continent	democratic	natural	nutrition

Example: *campaign*: a series of public actions to achieve a particular result

1. ______________: the process of getting the right food for good health and growth
2. ______________: one of the main areas of land on the earth
3. ______________: coming from nature; not made by people
4. ______________: a group of people chosen to do a particular job or make decisions
5. ______________: a system in which everyone has the same right to vote and speak

Use the words in the box at the top of the page to complete the sentences.

6. We had five steps in our ______________ to elect Lee.
7. Vegetables are a good source of ______________ to help you stay healthy.
8. Wool is a ______________ fiber, not one made by people.
9. In a ______________ government, the rule is "one vote, one person."
10. Asia is the largest ______________, and Australia is the smallest one.

VOCABULARY Academic Words *Use with textbook page 320.*

Read the paragraph below. Pay attention to the underlined academic words.

Modern medical technology keeps advancing. Companies continue to develop new machines and devices that help cure diseases and sustain life. Every available resource is needed to develop these products. Private businesses and investors usually finance the new inventions. Governments, concerned about the welfare of people who will use them, usually check each aspect of the technology before they approve the new devices.

Write the letter of the correct definition next to each word.

Example: ___f___ welfare

_____ **1.** technology

_____ **2.** resource

_____ **3.** aspect

_____ **4.** finance

_____ **5.** sustain

a. one of the parts or features of a situation, idea, or problem

b. something such as land, minerals, or natural energy that exists in a country and can be used in order to increase its wealth

c. make it possible for someone or something to continue to exist over time

d. provide money for something

e. a combination of all the knowledge, equipment, or methods used in scientific or industrial work

f. health, comfort, and happiness

Use the academic words from the exercise above to complete the sentences.

6. People need food and water to __________________ life.

7. Gold is a valuable natural __________________.

8. The class talked about one __________________ of the book.

Complete the sentences with your own ideas.

Example: You should study finance so you can ___manage your money___.

9. My favorite technology is ____________________________.

10. I sustain my good health by ____________________________.

Name ______________________________ Date ______________

WORD STUDY **Suffixes *-ic, -ist, -able*** *Use with textbook page 321.*

REMEMBER A *suffix* is a letter or letters added to the end of a word to make a new word. Suffixes can change a word's part of speech and meaning. If a base word ends in *e*, you usually drop the *e* when the suffix is added, as in *trombone* + *-ist* = *trombonist*, "one who plays the trombone."

Look at the chart below. Add the suffix *-ic, -ist,* or *-able* to create a new word. Write the new word in the chart. Then write the word's meaning and part of speech.

Word	Suffix	New Word	Meaning	Part of Speech
angel	*-ic*	*angelic*	*like an angel*	*adjective*
1. hero	*-ic*			
2. motor	*-ist*			
3. novel	*-ist*			
4. train	*-able*			
5. obtain	*-able*			

Create a new word by adding the suffix *-ic, -ist,* or *-able* to each word below. Then write the definition next to the new word. Check a dictionary if necessary.

Example: debate *+ able = debatable: able to be debated*

6. guitar ______________________________

7. wash ______________________________

8. idiot ______________________________

9. ideal ______________________________

10. explain ______________________________

READING STRATEGY | FOLLOW STEPS IN A PROCESS

Use with textbook page 321.

REMEMBER When you follow steps in a process, you read the instructions about how to do something. Usually, the steps are arranged in chronological, or time, order, from first to last.

Read the paragraph below. Then answer the questions that follow.

Making bread isn't easy, but you can do it if you follow the recipe. First, you mix the yeast with sugar and warm water and let it sit for a little while. Then you mix dry ingredients. After that you mix the wet ingredients. Then you mix them together. Next, put the lump of dough on a surface covered with flour and knead them with your hands for ten minutes. Put the dough in a bowl and let it rise for about an hour. Punch it down, then make it into loaves. Let it rise again. Then bake it.

1. What is the first step in making bread?

____

____

2. What is the last step before putting the bread in the oven?

____

____

3. What are some of the words in the passage that show a new step will follow?

____

____

4. What conclusions can you make about baking bread from reading these steps?

____

____

5. How can following steps in a process help you to become a better reader?

____

____

Name ______________________ Date ____________

COMPREHENSION

Use with textbook page 326.

Choose the best answer for each item. Circle the letter of the correct answer.

1. Wangari Maathai won the Nobel Prize for ______.

   a. working toward peace **b.** art and music **c.** being an excellent student

2. Maathai started an organization called ______.

   a. Kenyan Women **b.** the Green Belt Movement **c.** A Single Step

3. Some people in Kenya didn't like Maathai's ideas because she ______.

   a. always worked alone **b.** didn't finish school **c.** changed the way things are done

4. Maathai's main goal is to give people ______.

   a. a lot of money **b.** awards **c.** a better life

5. The first step in planting a tree is to ______.

   a. choose a good place **b.** put the tree in the hole **c.** water your tree

EXTENSION

Use with textbook page 327.

Write five ways that Wangari Maathai helped the world and people in the chart. Then write ways that you can help the world and people. The first answer has been done for you.

How Maathai Helped the World	How I Can Help the World
She convinced people to plant trees.	*I can plant some trees in my town.*

GRAMMAR **Imperatives** *Use with textbook page 328.*

REMEMBER Imperatives request that an action is performed. Imperatives are used to give instructions, directions, or orders, and to make suggestions or requests. The subject of an imperative sentence is rarely mentioned. It is generally understood that a *you* is addressed by the imperative.
Example: Don't drive too fast.
Imperatives are most commonly used in instruction booklets or other how-to writing.

Mark each imperative with a ✓.

Example: __✓__ Don't go out after dark!

______ I don't think you should go out after dark.

1. ______ Can you help me?

______ Help me!

2. ______ Turn off the light when you leave the room.

______ Would you mind turning off the light when leaving the room?

3. ______ It is best to turn right at the intersection.

______ Turn right at the intersection.

Rewrite each of the following sentences as an imperative. The first sentence has been done for you.

Example: You will be home on time.

Be home on time.

4. You will read every day.

____

5. You must work hard.

____

Name ______________________________ Date ______________

Sequence Words and Phrases *Use with textbook page 329.*

REMEMBER Sequencing words and phrases are often used with imperatives to give instructions. Use a comma after all these sequencing words except for *then*.

Read the instructions for how to plant a tree. Rewrite them in the correct order. Use correct punctuation.

How to plant a tree

Dig a hole.
Unwrap the rootball.
Choose a site.
Water the tree.
Put the tree in the hole.
Fill in the space around the rootball.

First ______________________________

Then ______________________________

Next ______________________________

After that ______________________________

Then ______________________________

Finally ______________________________

Number the instructions in the correct order. Then rewrite them in the correct order using sequence words.

How to make a pumpkin jack o'lantern

______ Close the top of the pumpkin. *First, cut a hole in the top of the pumpkin.*

__1__ Cut a hole in the top of the pumpkin. ______________________________

______ Cut out holes for the eyes and mouth. ______________________________

______ Light the candle. ______________________________

______ Put a candle inside the pumpkin. ______________________________

______ Put the pumpkin outside your front door. ______________________________

______ Scoop out the seeds. ______________________________

WRITING Write How-to Instructions *Use with textbook pages 330–331.*

Complete your own steps-in-a-process chart for a paragraph that gives instructions on how to do something.

Use the Peer Review Checklist below to obtain feedback from your partner. This feedback will help you edit your final draft.

PEER REVIEW CHECKLIST

- ☐ Does the paragraph give instructions for doing an activity?
- ☐ Are steps presented in a logical order?
- ☐ Do sequence words and phrases help clarify the steps?
- ☐ Is the imperative used correctly?
- ☐ Is each word spelled correctly?
- ☐ What changes could be made to improve the paragraph?

Name ________________________________ Date ____________

How are courage and imagination linked?

READING 3: From *Hoot*

VOCABULARY **Literary Words** *Use with textbook page 333.*

REMEMBER **Humor** is anything that makes people laugh or amuses them. Writers use words and images to create humor. Writers also use **colorful language** to amuse their readers. Idioms, hyperbole, and slang are all examples of colorful language. *The apple of my eye* is an idiom. *I could eat a cow!* is hyperbole. *Yo, dude!* is slang.

Label each sentence as *humor* or *colorful language*.

Literary Word	Example
humor	Did you see this headline? "Astronaut takes blame for gas in spacecraft."
1.	I heard the gossip straight from the horse's mouth.
2.	What's worse than finding a worm in your apple? Finding half a worm!
3.	She is as honest as the day is long.
4.	What is the laziest vegetable? A couch potato!
5.	Who let the cat out of the bag and spoiled the surprise?

Write a sentence that contains either humor or colorful language next to each line.

Literary Element	Sentence
colorful language	*Give me an honest answer and don't pull my leg!*
6. humor	
7. colorful language	
8. humor	
9. colorful language	
10. humor	

VOCABULARY **Academic Words** *Use with textbook page 334.*

Read the paragraph below. Pay attention to the underlined academic words.

An automobile company wants to build a factory next to the oldest park in our town. Almost everyone thinks this is a terrible <u>site</u> for a factory. The <u>image</u> of children playing and families picnicking right next to a factory is not at all attractive. Several groups are planning to <u>demonstrate</u> against the automobile company next week. They hope the city will <u>deny</u> the company's request to build a factory in that location.

Write the academic words from the paragraph above next to their correct definitions.

Example: ___site___: a place where something is being built or will be built

1. ____________: protest or support something in public with a lot of other people

2. ____________: a picture that you can see through a camera, on television, or in a mirror; a picture that you have in your mind

3. ____________: say that something is not true

Use the academic words from the paragraph above to complete the sentences.

4. Luci got a haircut and was shocked at her new ____________.

5. The protestors will ____________ against a store in place of the park.

6. The Atlantic Ocean is a new ____________ for energy windmills.

7. The children ____________ that they climbed the tree, but Mom knows they did.

Complete the sentences with your own ideas.

Example: The children see their image ___in the water___.

8. Here is one thing I can deny: ____________.

9. Something I would like to demonstrate against is ____________.

10. In my town, the best site to build a new athletic complex is ____________.

Name ______________________________ Date ____________

WORD STUDY **Prefixes *mega-, tele-, re-*** *Use with textbook page 335.*

REMEMBER A prefix is a word part added to the beginning of a word that changes the word's meaning. For example, the prefix *re-* means "again." When you add *re-* to *view*, the new word *review* means "to view again." Knowing the meanings of prefixes can help you figure out many unfamiliar words.

Look at the chart below. Add the prefixes *mega-, tele-,* or *re-* to each base word to create a new word. Write the new word and its meaning in the chart.

Prefix	Base Word	New Word	Definition
mega-	byte	*megabyte*	*a unit for measuring computer information equal to a million bytes*
1. *mega-*	watt		
2. *tele-*	graph		
3. *tele-*	phone		
4. *re-*	cycle		
5. *re-*	fuel		

Create a new word by adding the prefix *mega-, tele-,* or *re-* to each word below. Then write the definition next to the new word. Check a dictionary if necessary.

Example: generate *regenerate: to bring back to life*

6. unite ______________________________

7. vitamin ______________________________

8. commuter ______________________________

9. consider ______________________________

10. vision ______________________________

READING STRATEGY SUMMARIZE

Use with textbook page 335.

REMEMBER When you summarize fiction, you write a few sentences about what happens in the story. When you summarize nonfiction, you write a few sentences about the main ideas.

Read each paragraph. Then answer the questions that follow.

It was supposed to be a two-hour sailing trip off the Maine Coast. But a sudden storm had brewed up. The little sailboat crashed into some rocks on a deserted island. Ashley and Courtney had to climb onto the rocky shore as their boat sank. They shivered under spruce trees as cold rain pelted down on them. "The thing is," Courtney said, "I forgot to leave Mom a note to tell her what we were doing."

1. What happens in this story?

____

____

2. Summarize why the girls are in danger.

____

____

People in ancient Rome had a healthy diet. They ate a lot of vegetables, such as cabbage, cauliflower, and carrots. They also ate beans like chickpeas and lentils. They loved bread. If they were rich, they could enjoy meat and fish. One of their flavorings was a sauce called *garum*. It was made of rotten fish. They used it on everything.

3. What is the main idea of this text?

____

____

4. Summarize why the ancient Romans had a healthy diet.

____

____

5. How can the strategy of summarizing help you become a better reader?

____

____

Name ______________________________ Date ______________

COMPREHENSION

Use with textbook page 344.

Choose the best answer for each item. Circle the letter of the correct answer.

1. Roy and his friends are protesting against ______.

   a. owls **b.** summer school **c.** a new restaurant

2. Mullet Fingers claims the bucket is filled with ______.

   a. snapping turtles **b.** bad poison **c.** live cottonmouth snakes

3. The bucket is really filled with ______.

   a. huge spiders **b.** toy snakes **c.** angry bees

4. By the end of the story, Mother Paula is on the same side as ______.

   a. Chuck E. Muckle **b.** the restaurant owners **c.** Mullet Fingers

5. Chuck E. Muckle stands for ______.

   a. selfish, greedy people **b.** people who like pancakes **c.** all rich people

RESPONSE TO LITERATURE

Use with textbook page 345.

Imagine that you are Roy. How can you solve Mullet Fingers' problem? Write at least five lines.

____

____

____

____

____

____

____

____

____

____

GRAMMAR **Reported Speech** *Use with textbook page 346.*

REMEMBER Reported speech is used to tell what another person has said. There is a phrase with a reporting verb, such as *say*, and a noun clause.

Complete the sentences with the correct form of the verb.

1. "We won't let you hurt the owls," he said.

   He said he ________________ let them hurt the owls.

2. "There are no owls here," he said.

   He said there ________________ no owls there.

3. "I took pictures of the owls," he said.

   He said he ________________ pictures of the owls.

4. "The owls don't have a chance against the machines," he said.

   He said the owls ________________ a chance against the machines.

Rewrite each sentence as reported speech. Change pronouns and verbs if necessary.

5. He said, "It's time to start."

   ____

6. She said, "I'll see you next spring."

   ____

7. They said, "We're not going to eat your pancakes."

   ____

8. He said, "You didn't check your facts."

   ____

Name ______________________________ Date ______________

Reported Speech: Questions, Imperatives, *told* *Use with textbook page 347.*

REMEMBER When reporting a question, you can use the reporting verb *ask*.
Example: She asked what the matter was.
When reporting an imperative, change the imperative to an infinitive.
Example: She said to be careful.
Use *told* when you want to say who the person is speaking to. An object must always follow *told*.
Example: She told us there was no need to worry.

Choose the correct way to complete each sentence.

1. She asked what time _______.

   a. it was **b.** was it

2. They asked us _______.

   a. be quiet **b.** to be quiet

3. We asked them _______.

   a. not to shout **b.** to not shout

4. He asked what _______.

   a. did we see **b.** we saw

5. They told _______.

   a. to go home **b.** us to go home

Complete the sentences.

6. "What's the problem?" he asked.

   He asked ______________________________.

7. "Where will we meet?" they asked.

   They asked ______________________________.

8. "Don't take pictures," he said.

   He said ______________________________.

9. "Please go away," he told us.

   He told ______________________________.

10. "Where did they go?" he asked us.

    He asked ______________________________.

WRITING Write a Plot Summary *Use with textbook pages 348–349.*

Complete your own plot summary chart for a paragraph that summarizes the plot of a story, novel, movie, or television show.

Main characters and setting:

Characters' goals:

Main events:
1.
2.
3.

Outcome:

Use the Peer Review Checklist below to obtain feedback from your partner. This feedback will help you edit your final draft.

PEER REVIEW CHECKLIST

- ☐ Does the paragraph summarize a plot?
- ☐ Are the characters and setting briefly described?
- ☐ Does the summary include only the main events?
- ☐ Are newly acquired vocabulary words used accurately?
- ☐ Is reported speech used correctly?
- ☐ What changes could be made to improve the summary?

Name ______________________________ Date ______________

How are courage and imagination linked?

READING 4: "Between Two Worlds"

VOCABULARY **Key Words** *Use with textbook page 351.*

Write each word in the box next to its definition.

armies	captured	gifted	nomads	tepees	reservations

Example: ___tepees___: large round tents with pointed tops, used in past times by some Native Americans

1. ______________: areas of land that are kept separate for Native Americans to live on
2. ______________: caught by a person or animal in order to be kept somewhere
3. ______________: members of a group of people that move from place to place to find food
4. ______________: military forces that fight on land
5. ______________: having the natural ability to do something very well

Use the words in the box at the top of the page to complete the sentences.

6. The people are going to build new roads and schools on the ______________.
7. The ______________ fought for two years, and then the governments agreed to stop.
8. He is very ______________ in languages. He speaks English, Chinese, and Spanish.
9. The ______________ helped protect the families from bad weather.
10. The police have ______________ the person who stole the money from the bank.

VOCABULARY **Academic Words** *Use with textbook page 352.*

Read the paragraph below. Pay attention to the underlined academic words.

> My brother and his wife decided to <u>construct</u> a new home in Vail, Colorado. They chose to live in a <u>region</u> with snow and mountains because they like to ski. I couldn't help but <u>react</u> with excitement when I heard about their new home. I love to ski, too! When the <u>circumstances</u> are right, I'll ask if I can come for a visit.

Write the letter of the correct definition next to each word.

Example: ___c___ region

______ **1.** react

______ **2.** construct

______ **3.** circumstances

a. the facts or conditions that affect a situation, action, or event

b. build something large such as a building, bridge, or sculpture

c. a fairly large area of a state, country, and so on

d. behave in a particular way because of what someone has done or said to you

Use the academic words from the exercise above to complete the sentences.

4. The tri-state ________________ includes New York, New Jersey, and Connecticut.

5. My dogs always ________________ to visitors by barking a lot.

6. Students can leave the classroom only under certain ________________.

7. Rick plans to ________________ a model of the museum from wooden blocks.

Complete the sentences with your own ideas.

Example: The circumstances surrounding the burglary were very ___*mysterious*___.

8. When I have a problem, I react by ________________________.

9. The states in my region include ________________________.

10. If I could build anything I wanted, I would construct

________________________.

Name ________________________________ Date ______________

WORD STUDY **Spelling Words with *ea*** *Use with textbook page 353.*

REMEMBER Two vowels can work as a team to stand for one vowel sound. The vowel team *ea* can stand for the long vowel /ē/ as in *treat*. It can also stand for the short vowel /e/ as in *spread*. In a few words, *ea* stands for the long vowel /ā/ as in *steak*. Knowing these sound spellings can help you say and spell many words correctly.

Read the words in the box below quietly to yourself. Notice what sound the vowel team *ea* stands for in each word. Then sort the words according to their sound spellings. Write each word in the correct column in the chart.

~~wreath~~	dread	great	sheath	bread
break	thread	cheat	break-in	

/ē/ spelled *ea*	/e/ spelled *ea*	/ā/ spelled *ea*
wreath		

Identify what sound the vowel digraph *ea* stands for in each word below. Then use each word in a sentence of your own.

Example: instead *ea stands for /e/ I wore a scarf instead of a hat.*

1. seal ______________________________
2. bleach ______________________________
3. breakthrough ______________________________
4. dream ______________________________
5. feather ______________________________
6. widespread ______________________________
7. leaf ______________________________

READING STRATEGY CLASSIFY

Use with textbook page 353.

REMEMBER When you classify, you arrange words, ideas, objects, texts, or people into groups with common characteristics.

Read each paragraph. Then answer the questions that follow.

Luisa loved sports. She was always playing softball, hockey, or soccer. Her brother Luis loved cooking. His dad taught him to make fried eggs and oatmeal when he was five. By the time he was eight, he could bake a cake from scratch and make pie crusts. At age ten, he could make an asparagus soufflé. Luisa loved his spaghetti with meat sauce. He always made it for her before she played a big game. She called it Luis's Lucky Spaghetti.

1. What words in this passage have to do with sports?

____

____

2. What words in this passage have to do with food?

____

____

Ben's mom was in the army, so the family often moved from place to place. He was born in Ohio. The family lived in Germany when he was two. When he was six, they moved to Japan. One day, they went to a kite festival, and Ben fell in love with kites. When they moved to Florida, he flew a flat kite on the beach. In Kansas, he learned to fly a box kite. Then, when they moved to Oklahoma, he learned how to fly a sports kite.

3. What words in this passage have to do with different types of kites?

____

4. What words in this passage have to do with places?

____

5. How do you think classifying can make you a better reader?

____

____

Name ______________________________ Date ______________

COMPREHENSION *Use with textbook page 358.*

Choose the best answer for each item. Circle the letter of the correct answer.

1. The Comanches could talk to ______.

   a. only other Comanches **b.** only other Native Americans **c.** many different people

2. The Parker family wanted to ______ , so they built a fort.

   a. stay safe **b.** work hard **c.** attack others

3. Cynthia Ann's ideas about the Comanches ______.

   a. were always good **b.** were always bad **c.** changed over time

4. Reservations were places where ______ wanted to live.

   a. only the white settlers **b.** nobody **c.** everybody

5. The most important thing to Quanah was ______.

   a. his people **b.** his land **c.** the white settlers

EXTENSION *Use with textbook page 359.*

The reading "Between Two Worlds" talks about both good events and bad events. In the column on the left, list good events from the story. In the column on the right, list bad events from the story.

Good Events	Bad Events

GRAMMAR Active Voice and Passive Voice

Use with textbook page 360.

REMEMBER Use the active voice when the focus is on who or what does the action, also called the performer. Use the passive voice when the focus is on the receiver of the action. A *by*-phrase is used to identify the performer. To form the passive voice, use *be* + the past participle.
Example: The children were taken to school by their parents.

Are the sentences active or passive?

	Active	Passive
1. The Comanche traveled from place to place.	☐	☐
2. Berries and plants were gathered by the women.	☐	☐
3. Cynthia Ann was captured by the Comanche.	☐	☐
4. They taught her the Comanche language.	☐	☐
5. The whites captured her and locked her in a room.	☐	☐

Rewrite each sentence by using the verb in the passive voice.

6. They built settlements near the Navasota River.

____

7. At first they did not treat her well.

____

8. Then they gave her to a Comanche couple.

____

9. They sent the Comanches to live on reservations.

____

Name ______________________________ Date ______________

Passive Voice: Omitting the *by*-phrase *Use with textbook page 361.*

REMEMBER A *by*-phrase is used in passive voice sentences when it is important to know the performer of the action.
Example: She was captured by the Comanches.
When the performer of the action is unimportant or unknown, the *by*-phrase is omitted.
Example: She was taught the Comanche language.

Rewrite the sentences, changing them from active voice to passive voice. Include the by-phrase if necessary.

1. They built the house in 1922.

____

2. Henry James wrote this story.

____

3. People speak Portuguese in Brazil.

____

4. They produce this newspaper in New York.

____

5. The Inca built Machu Pichu in the fifteenth century.

____

Write sentences using the passive voice.

6. the telephone / invent / Alexander Graham Bell

____

7. the Statue of Liberty / design / Bertholdi

____

8. "Romeo and Juliet" and "Hamlet" / write / Shakespeare

____

9. the Pyramids / build / the Egyptians

____

WRITING AN EXPOSITORY PARAGRAPH

Write a Paragraph That Classifies *Use with textbook pages 362–363.*

Complete your own chart for a paragraph about three types of art that you enjoy.

Use the Peer Review Checklist below to obtain feedback from your partner. This feedback will help you edit your final draft.

PEER REVIEW CHECKLIST

- ☐ Does the paragraph classify three types of art?
- ☐ Are similar items grouped together by category?
- ☐ Are the features of each category clearly defined?
- ☐ Do sentences vary in length and pattern?
- ☐ Does the writer use the active and passive voice correctly?
- ☐ What changes could be made to improve the paragraph?

Name ______________________________ Date ______________

WRITING WORKSHOP *Use with textbook pages 368–371.*

Organize your ideas in the graphic organizer below.

Problem	*Solution*

Use the Peer Review Checklist below to obtain feedback from your partner. This feedback will help you edit your final draft.

PEER REVIEW CHECKLIST

- ☐ Does the essay hold my interest and attention?
- ☐ Does it include specific examples, details, and explanations?
- ☐ Does the order of information fit the topic?
- ☐ Does the writer use the active and passive voice correctly?
- ☐ Does the writer use imperatives correctly?
- ☐ What changes could be made to improve the essay?

LEARNING LOG

Use after completing page 372.

Underline the vocabulary items you know and can use well. Review and practice any you haven't underlined. Underline them when you know them well.

Literary Words	Key Words	Academic Words	
setting the scene	armies	approach	image
list of characters	captured	convey	site
stage directions	gifted	cooperate	circumstances
humor	nomads	drama	construct
colorful language	tepees	aspect	react
	reservation	finance	region
	campaign	resource	
	committee	sustain	
	continent	technology	
	democratic	welfare	
	natural	demonstrate	
	nutrition	deny	

Put a check by the skills you can perform well. Review and practice any you haven't checked off. Check them off when you can perform them well.

Skills	I can . . .
Word Study	☐ spell words with *oo*. ☐ recognize and use the suffixes *-ic*, *-ist*, and *-able*. ☐ recognize and use the prefixes *mega-*, *tele-*, and *re-*. ☐ spell words with *ea*.
Reading Strategies	☐ analyze text structure. ☐ follow steps in a process. ☐ summarize. ☐ classify.
Grammar	☐ use *be going to* and *will*. ☐ use imperatives and sequence words and phrases. ☐ use reported speech. ☐ use active voice and passive voice.
Writing	☐ write a formal e-mail. ☐ write how-to instructions. ☐ write a plot summary. ☐ write a paragraph that classifies. ☐ write an expository essay.

Test Preparation

TEST 1

DIRECTIONS
Read this selection. Then answer the questions that follow it.

The Fair Trade Movement

1 The fair trade movement began in the 1940s and 1950s. Groups tried to sell products made in poor countries to markets in rich countries. Most of the first products sold were craft items. Women made most of these items while they cared for their children.

2 There are now many fair trade products you can buy. Some of the products include coffee, cocoa, tea, chocolate, clothing, and cotton. People make or grow these products in groups called <u>cooperatives</u>.

3 Fair trade organizations must meet certain requirements. Buyers have to pay the farmers or producers a minimum price. The farmers and producers have to guarantee their workers a living wage and safe working conditions. Fair trade organizations have to invest some of the money they make in the community where they do business.

4 The fair trade movement has its supporters and critics. People who support it say it helps farmers and producers gain <u>access</u> to markets. Critics feel fair trade standards are too strict, or not strict enough. Whether we agree or disagree with the fair trade movement, we know it is here to stay.

1 A <u>cooperative</u> is ______.

- **A** people or groups acting alone
- **B** people or groups working together
- **C** a very large company
- **D** a place to buy organic food

2 If Maria wants to gain <u>access</u> to something, what does she want to gain?

- **F** entry
- **G** discounts
- **H** promises
- **J** profits

TEST 2

DIRECTIONS
Read this selection. Then answer the questions that follow it.

New Home

1 Abby felt sad and lonely as she looked out the window of the bus. Her family had moved to Cedar Park two months ago. She had met a few girls, but it was hard to make friends in a new place. As the bus drove toward her street, she saw a group of girls playing soccer. They were smiling and laughing. She wished she could play soccer with them.

2 Abby got off the bus and looked at the girls. She thought about asking if she could play with them, but she felt shy. What would she say? After a moment, Abby turned around and walked to her house.

3 Abby's mom was in the kitchen. She gave Abby an apple and asked if she had met any new friends that day. Abby shook her head.

4 Suddenly Abby knew what she had to do. "Mom, I saw a group of girls playing soccer outside. I think they would be fun to play with. I just need to be brave and introduce myself."

5 "Go play, Abby," said her mom. "They would probably like to have another player."

6 Abby walked outside and stopped. She watched the girls kick the ball for a second. Then she took a deep breath and started walking.

1 What is paragraph 1 mainly about?

- **A** How Abby feels about moving
- **B** What Abby plans to do after school
- **C** What Abby likes to do
- **D** What sports girls in Cedar Park play

2 The selection is best described as —

- **F** informative
- **G** entertaining
- **H** persuasive
- **J** factual

3 The reader can predict that Abby will —

- **A** decide to go back home
- **B** teach the girls to make a goal
- **C** ride the bus home from school
- **D** introduce herself to the girls

4 According to the selection, Abby is unhappy because —

- **F** she wants to play soccer
- **G** she has moved to a new city
- **H** she misses her old friends
- **J** no one has asked her to play

Name ______________________________ Date ______________

TEST 3

DIRECTIONS
Read this selection. Then answer the questions that follow it.

The Solar System

1 What do you see in the sky at night? The moon. Stars. Planets. Every object you see in the sky is part of the Milky Way galaxy. A galaxy is a group of stars, planets, gases, and dust. Earth, the planet we live on, is part of the Milky Way galaxy.

2 A galaxy has many solar systems in it. A solar system is a group of objects that orbit a star. Earth is part of a solar system that has eight planets that all orbit the sun.

What is it like on other planets?

3 The first four planets in our solar system are Mercury, Venus, Earth, and Mars. They are closer to the sun than the other planets. They are made mostly of rock. Mercury is closest to the sun. The sun's heat makes the planet hot and dry. It is covered with holes called craters. Mercury is small—about one-third the size of Earth.

4 Venus is hotter than Mercury. This is because of Venus's atmosphere. Clouds of gases cover the planet. The thick clouds trap the heat.

5 Earth is the only planet that we know has life. Earth has oxygen. Oxygen is a gas that animals and people need to breathe. Earth is also the only planet with liquid water. Water covers more than 70 percent of Earth's surface. That's why people sometimes call Earth "the blue planet."

6 Mars is farther from the sun than Earth, so it is colder than Earth. Mars has a red, rocky surface. It is often called "the red planet."

7 Jupiter, Saturn, Uranus, and Neptune are the outer planets. They are far from the sun and very cold. Jupiter is the largest planet in the solar system. It is very windy. Saturn is the second largest planet. It has bright rings that are easy to see. Uranus is the seventh planet from the sun. It has thin, dark rings. Neptune, the next planet, is also very windy. Storms on Neptune can last hundreds of years!

1 Look at the chart.

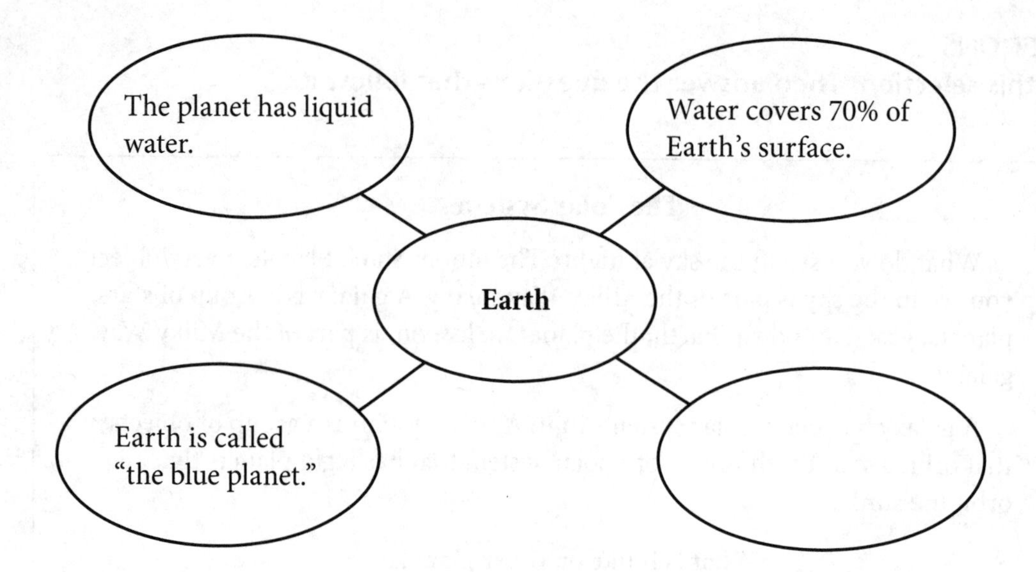

Which of the following facts should be added to the chart?

A Mars is farther from the sun.
B Earth has oxygen.
C Mars is colder than Earth.
D Oxygen is a gas.

2 Paragraph 7 is mainly about —

F the outer planets
G stars
H craters
J water on Earth

3 In paragraph 5, what words help the reader know what *oxygen* means?

A a gas that animals and people need to breathe
B has life
C covers more than 70 percent
D liquid water

4 According to the article, why is Earth sometimes called "the blue planet"?

F Earth is the only planet with life.
G Earth has oxygen.
H Water covers more than 70 percent of the Earth's surface.
J Earth is the only planet with liquid water.

Name ______________________________ Date ______________

Visual Literacy: Smithsonian American Art Museum *Use with textbook pages 374–375.*

LEARNING TO LOOK

Look at *The Throne of the Third Heaven of the Nations' Millennium General Assembly* by James Hampton on page 375 in your textbook. Link to the Smithsonian American Art Museum web site feature http://americanart.si.edu/collections/interact/zoom/hampton_throne.cfm. Zoom in on Hampton's throne in more detail. Focus on one section of the artwork. List as many details as possible about that one section.

Example: *There is a silver frame on the wall.*

1. ______________________________
2. ______________________________
3. ______________________________
4. ______________________________
5. ______________________________

INTERPRETATION

Look at *The Throne of the Third Heaven of the Nations' Millennium General Assembly* again. Imagine that you could create a work of art out of everyday objects like Hampton did. List the objects you would use.

Example: *light bulb*

6. ______________________________
7. ______________________________
8. ______________________________
9. ______________________________
10. ______________________________

Where would you display it? Why?

____

____

5W&H

Look at *The Throne of the Third Heaven of the Nations' Millennium General Assembly* by James Hampton again. If you could interview James Hampton about this work of art, what would you ask him? Use *Who, What, Why, Where, When,* and *How* to frame your questions.

Example: Where did you find all of the objects that you used?

11. Who ______________________

____

12. Where ______________________

____

13. When ______________________

____

14. What ______________________

____

15. Why ______________________

____

16. How ______________________

____

Name ______________________________ Date ______________

UNIT 6

What is your vision of life in the future?

READING 1: *"Life in the Future"*

VOCABULARY **Key Words** *Use with textbook page 379.*

Write each word in the box next to its definition.

artificial	canyons	frontier	mass-produced	~~robots~~	volcanoes

Example: ___robots___: machines that move and can do some of the work of humans.

1. ______________: the area beyond the places people know well
2. ______________: mountains with a large hole on top out of which lava, rock, and ashes sometimes explode
3. ______________: not real or natural, but made by people
4. ______________: produced in large numbers using machinery so that each object is the same and can be sold cheaply
5. ______________: deep valleys with very steep sides

Use the words in the box at the top of the page to complete the sentences.

6. ______________ that erupt underwater can cause huge waves.
7. Many ______________ do work that is too dangerous for humans.
8. The ______________ flowers look real!
9. The Southwest has many deep ______________, but the Midwest is very flat.
10. Some people say that the sea is the last unexplored ______________.

VOCABULARY **Academic Words** *Use with textbook page 380.*

Read the paragraph below. Pay attention to the underlined academic words.

"Green" is the new <u>trend</u> in home design. The <u>occupation</u> of a green architect is to <u>research</u> what building materials and technology will be least harmful to the environment. Solar panels are a popular part of green design because their <u>function</u> is to use the natural rays of sunlight to power a home. Using natural energy and environmentally friendly materials is good for the planet and also usually saves money.

Write the academic words from the paragraph above next to their correct definitions.

Example: *function*: the usual purpose of a thing, or the job that someone usually does

1. ____________________: job or profession

2. ____________________: serious study of a subject that is intended to discover new facts about it

3. ____________________: the way a situation is generally developing or changing

Use the academic words from the paragraph above to complete the sentences.

4. The scientist does ____________________ on diseases to try to find cures for them.

5. The latest fashion ____________________ for women is flat shoes.

6. The ____________________ of a fuse is to control electricity in a home.

7. Her ____________________ is teaching at the high school.

Complete the sentences with your own ideas.

Example: I have noticed a trend *toward early retirement and part-time jobs*.

8. I want to do research on ______________________________.

9. The function of a car is to ______________________________.

10. The occupation I want when I grow up is ______________________________.

Name ______________________________ Date ______________

WORD STUDY Spelling the Diphthongs /oi/ and /ou/

Use with textbook page 381.

REMEMBER Some English words contain two vowel sounds that are said quickly so that the sounds glide into one another. The two sounds form a vowel sound called a diphthong. **Example:** *boil*

Look at the words in the word box. Write each word in the chart below under the column it belongs in and circle the diphthong in each word.

~~foil~~	mouse	brow	soy	proud	choice
voyage	broil	sound	frown	allow	employ

/oi/ as in *coin*	/oi/ as in *boy*	/ou/ as in *ground*	/ou/ as in *how*
foil			

Write two sentences with words that contain the /oi/ sound spelled *oi* or *oy* as indicated in parentheses.

1. (*oi*) ______________________________

2. (*oy*) ______________________________

Write two sentences with words that contain the /ou/ sound spelled *ou* or *ow* as indicated in parentheses.

3. (*ou*) ______________________________

4. (*ow*) ______________________________

READING STRATEGY **TAKE NOTES** *Use with textbook page 381.*

REMEMBER When you read, take notes. Keep track of the main idea and the details.

Read each paragraph. Then answer the questions that follow.

China is an ancient civilization that has contributed a great deal to the world. Thousands of years ago, the Chinese invented paper, the compass, gunpowder and printing. It is difficult to imagine life today without these inventions.

1. What is the main idea of the passage above?

____

____

2. What are the details in the passage above?

____

____

India is the largest democracy in the world. It is the second most highly populated country in the world after China. In terms of land mass, it is the seventh largest country on Earth.

3. What is the main idea of the passage above?

____

____

4. What are the details in the passage above?

____

____

5. How can the strategy of taking notes help you to understand what you read more clearly?

____

____

Name ______________________________ Date ______________

COMPREHENSION

Use with textbook page 388.

Choose the best answer for each item. Circle the letter of the correct answer.

1. Today, the world's population is ______.

a. growing fast **b.** shrinking fast **c.** staying the same

2. A hypersonic plane will most likely ______.

a. fly slowly **b.** fly very fast **c.** cost very little

3. Jetpacks will let people ______.

a. fly without planes **b.** stay healthy **c.** be in movies

4. The authors think the future will most likely have many ______.

a. creatures from outer space **b.** rich people **c.** wonderful inventions

5. The authors imagine the future as ______.

a. different from today **b.** worse than today **c.** the same as today

EXTENSION

Use with textbook page 389.

This article tells about the future. In the left column, write what the article says will happen in the future. In the right column, write what you think will happen. The first one is done for you.

What the Article Says about the Future	What I Think about the Future
Robots: *Some countries will have more robots than people*	*Robots will never become popular.*
Cities:	
Cars:	
Planes:	
Jetpacks:	
Living on Other Planets:	

GRAMMAR **Transitions** *Use with textbook pages 390–391.*

REMEMBER You can use transitional words such as the conjunctive adverbs *also* and *furthermore* to add information to a statement. These usually begin a statement or clause. You can also use the transitional phrases *in addition* and *as well.* These can come at the beginning or end of a statement. When a transition connects two sentences, use a period. When it connects two independent clauses, use a semicolon (;). When it begins a sentence or clause, use a comma after the transition.

Choose the best way to complete each sentence.

1. The birth rate is higher than the death rate. Also, ______.

a. people are living longer **b.** the population will be 11 billion

2. The apartment buildings will have high-speed elevators. In addition, ______.

a. people will never have to leave **b.** they will have stores, restaurants, and cinemas

3. People will explore new planets. Furthermore, ______.

a. they may start to colonize Mars **b.** it takes six months to reach Mars

Combine these sentences using the transitions in parentheses. Use correct punctuation.

4. It will be necessary to rebuild some cities. They will build some new ones. (also)

____

5. These new planes will fly faster. They will fly to outer space. (as well)

____

6. Cars will be safer. They will steer themselves. (furthermore)

____

7. For people to live on Mars, they will need to build giant domes. All food will have to be grown in the domes. (in addition)

____

Name ______________________________ Date ____________

Transitions *Use with textbook pages 390–391.*

REMEMBER The following transitions contrast two ideas: *instead, on the contrary, on the other hand* (often used with *on the one hand*). The following transitions show cause and effect: *as a result, thus, therefore, consequently.* Transitions can begin a sentence or can be used after a semicolon.

Choose the best way to complete each sentence.

1. People will not drive their own cars. Instead, ______.

   a. cars will be faster **b.** cars will steer themselves

2. More people will have cars. As a result, ______.

   a. the roads will be more crowded **b.** cars will be safer

3. People have already explored most of our planet. On the other hand, ______.

   a. many planets are still unknown **b.** many planets are far away

4. People want to live on Mars. Therefore, ______.

   a. they will have to build giant domes **b.** they cannot survive in the atmosphere

Combine these sentences using the transitions in parentheses. Use correct punctuation.

5. The world population is growing. There may not be enough food or space for everyone to live on this planet. (as a result)

   ____

6. There won't be space for everyone to live in houses. They will live in tall apartment buildings. (instead)

   ____

7. It takes a long time to fly to other planets. They will have to build faster planes. (therefore)

   ____

8. It is likely that people will travel to Mars. It takes six months to get there and Mars has no breathable oxygen. (on the other hand)

   ____

WRITING Write an Introductory Paragraph

Use with textbook pages 392–393.

Complete your own inverted pyramid to narrow a topic related to life in the future.

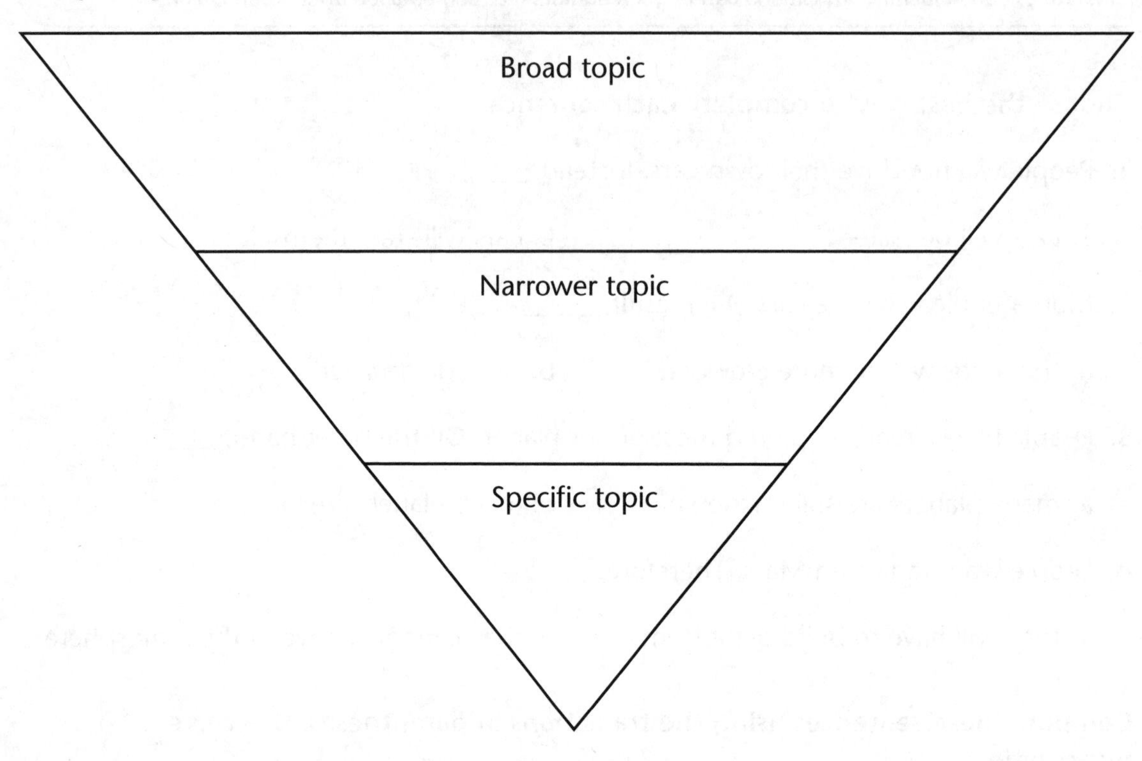

Use the Peer Review Checklist below to obtain feedback from your partner. This feedback will help you edit your final draft.

PEER REVIEW CHECKLIST

- ☐ Does the paragraph focus on a topic related to the future?
- ☐ Has the writer narrowed the topic effectively?
- ☐ Has the writer stated the topic clearly?
- ☐ Does the writing voice show knowledge of the topic?
- ☐ Do transitions connect ideas and information?
- ☐ What changes could be made to improve the paragraph?

Name ______________________________ Date ______________

What is your vision of life in the future?

READING 2: "Southbound on the Freeway" / "Cardinal Ideograms" / "Interview with an Astronaut: Dan Bursch"

VOCABULARY **Literary Words** *Use with textbook page 395.*

REMEMBER Writers make comparisons with **metaphors** and **similes**. Similes use *like* or *as*. *John is a bear* is a metaphor. *John is like a bear* is a simile. Poems are written in groups of lines called **stanzas**. A stanza can have any number of lines.

Label each sentence *metaphor, simile,* or *stanza.*

Sense	Description
metaphor	The winter sky is a dirty grey blanket.
1.	The goldenrod is yellow and the corn is turning brown, The trees in apple orchards with fruit are bending down.
2.	Life is like a playground, with so many fun things to do!
3.	No man is an island.
4.	Playing the trumpet is like flying in the sky.
5.	We were crowded in the cabin, Not a soul would dare to sleep— It was midnight on the waters, And storm was on the deep.

Read the poem "Summer." Label the underlined parts as *metaphor, simile,* or *stanza.*

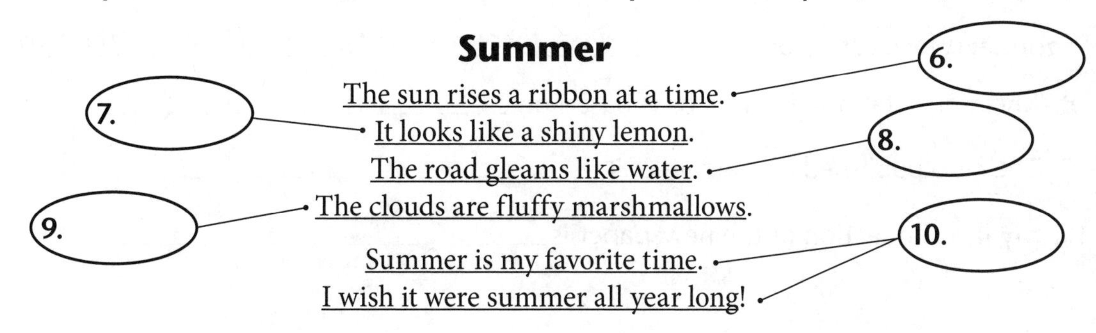

Summer
6.
The sun rises a ribbon at a time.
7.
It looks like a shiny lemon.
8.
The road gleams like water.
9.
The clouds are fluffy marshmallows.
10.
Summer is my favorite time.
I wish it were summer all year long!

VOCABULARY **Academic Words** *Use with textbook page 396.*

Read the paragraph below. Pay attention to the underlined academic words.

> Our book club meets once a month in the lounge section of our public library. We mostly read books that have been published recently. Sometimes the books concern fairly simple themes, and sometimes they are more complex. One of my favorite parts of the meetings is when everyone shares their interpretation of the book.

Write the letter of the correct definition next to each word.

Example: ___c___ section

_____ **1.** published   **a.** complicated

_____ **2.** complex   **b.** an explanation

_____ **3.** interpretation   **c.** a part of something

d. printed and sold

Use the academic words from the exercise above to complete the sentences.

4. We live in the northern _______________ of town.

5. The directions were so _______________ that no one understood them!

6. My sister's _______________ of the cave painting is the same as mine.

7. Cesar _______________ a story about his life in America.

Complete the sentences with your own ideas.

Example: A race car is complex, *because there are many parts that run together*.

8. My interpretation of paintings is based on _______________.

9. The club published a schedule of its _______________.

10. My favorite section of the newspaper is _______________.

Name ______________________ Date ______________

WORD STUDY **Greek and Latin Roots** *Use with textbook page 397.*

REMEMBER Many English words come from Greek and Latin word parts called roots. Knowing the meaning of a Greek or Latin root can help you figure out the meaning of a new word.
Example: The prefix *uni-* means one. A *uniform* means *one particular type of clothing worn by all members of a group.*

Review the prefixes and roots in the chart.

Prefixes		Roots	
uni- ("one") bi- ("two")	tri- ("three") re- ("again")	cycle ("round") spec ("see")	verse ("turn")

Look at the words below. In each word, underline any prefixes or roots from the chart above. Think about how the prefix or root helps you understand the meaning. Then write a definition of each word. Use a dictionary if needed.

Example: unite *to bring together*

1. triangle ______________________
2. spectator ______________________
3. recycle ______________________
4. unique ______________________
5. trilogy ______________________
6. reverse ______________________
7. billion ______________________
8. spectacular ______________________
9. bilingual ______________________
10. biweekly ______________________

Write sentences using one of the words you defined in the exercise above.

11. ______________________
12. ______________________
13. ______________________

READING STRATEGY | ANALYZE TEXT STRUCTURE 2

Use with textbook page 397.

REMEMBER When you read, analyze text structure by noticing how the text is presented. A poem is presented in stanzas. A script contains the names of characters in all caps, followed by a colon. After the colon, the character's lines of dialogue are presented.

Read each passage and answer the questions that follow.

Rose petals are red
Bluebirds are blue
Everything we said
Is perfectly true

1. What is the text structure of the passage above? How do you know?

____

JAMES: Where is the party?
JOHN: What party?
JAMES: The party that Alex and Sonia are throwing.
JOHN: I didn't even know they were throwing a party!

2. What is the text structure of the passage above? How do you know?

____

3. What do the names in all capital letters represent?

____

4. What does text after a colon represent in the passage above?

____

5. How can the strategy of analyzing text structure help you to understand what you read?

____

Name ______________________________ Date ______________

COMPREHENSION *Use with textbook page 406.*

Choose the best answer for each item. Circle the letter of the correct answer.

1. The tourist in "Southbound on the Freeway" decides that people on Earth are ______.

   a. measuring tapes **b.** cars **c.** worms

2. The poem "Cardinal Ideograms" describes ______.

   a. numbers **b.** people from outer space **c.** birds

3. Astronaut Dan Bursch finds being in space ______.

   a. boring **b.** just like being on Earth **c.** interesting

4. The tourist in "Southbound on the Freeway" and the speaker in "Cardinal Ideograms" look at common things ______.

   a. in the same way **b.** in new ways **c.** from outer space

5. The two poems and the interview are the same because they all describe ______.

   a. seeing familiar things in a new way **b.** life on another planet **c.** flying around Earth

RESPONSE TO LITERATURE *Use with textbook page 407.*

Write a short poem about what you think Earth will be like in 100 years. Try to use information from the two poems and the interview.

____

____

____

____

____

____

____

____

____

GRAMMAR General Rules of Capitalization *Use with textbook page 408.*

REMEMBER Capitalize the first word of a sentence. Capitalize proper nouns, such as names of people, including initials, countries/cities, languages/nationalities, organizations. Capitalize certain dates, such as days of the week and months of the year. Capitalize all words in a title, except for articles and shorter prepositions, unless they are the first or last word.

Which word in each group should NOT have a capital? Circle the answer.

1. Monday	Today	February	April
2. French	Italy	Kansas	Country
3. Brother	Lisa	New York	the United Nations
4. Arkansas	December	Month	Congress

Correct the errors in capitalization. Explain the rule for each error.

	Explanation
5. My name is Elizabeth t Wilson.	*Capitalize names of people including initials.*
6. My family is from canada.	______________
7. my sister's name is Elsa.	______________
8. We live in san francisco.	______________
9. My birthday is on june 10.	______________
10. The title is: "is there life on mars?"	______________

Name ______________________________ Date ______________

Capitalization: Abbreviations, Initials, and Special Terms

Use with textbook page 409.

REMEMBER With abbreviations of street names, capitalize the first letter. With abbreviations of states or countries, capitalize all letters. All letters of acronyms are capitalized. Some other terms that are capitalized include ship names (including spaceships), solar systems, and planets. (Exceptions are *sun* and *moon*.) When a noun is a company trademark, it is also capitalized.

Write the abbreviations or acronyms for these words.

1. Street ______________

2. Avenue ______________

3. Boulevard ______________

4. Road ______________

5. Maine ______________

6. Arizona ______________

7. Ohio ______________

8. Hawaii ______________

9. United Nations ______________

10. International Space Station ______________

11. National Aeronautics and Space Administration ______________

12. University of Illinois at Champaign ______________

Circle the letters that should be capitalized in this paragraph.

My name is dan. I have been on the international space station since february. i am here with my co-astronauts carl and yuri. yuri is from Russia. we eat american and russian food. we want to go to mars one day.

WRITING Support a Main Idea with Examples

Use with textbook pages 410–411.

Complete your own main idea/examples web for a paragraph about space missions or astronauts.

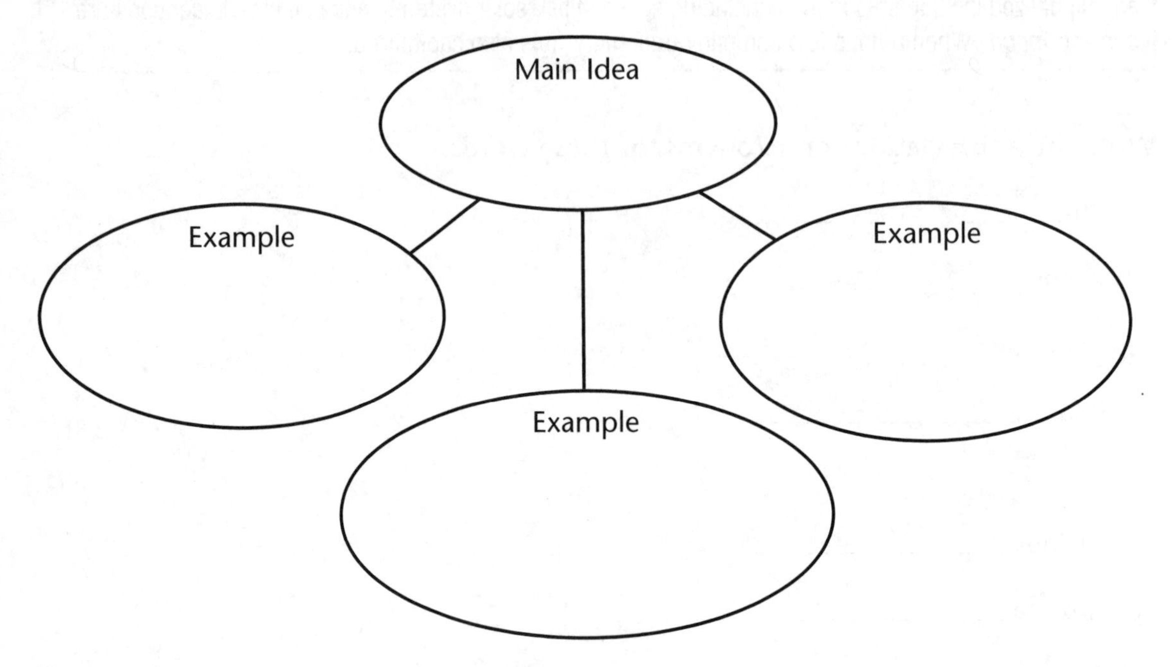

Use the Peer Review Checklist below to obtain feedback from your partner. This feedback will help you edit your final draft.

PEER REVIEW CHECKLIST

- ☐ Does the paragraph present a main idea?
- ☐ Is the main idea supported by at least three examples?
- ☐ Do the types of examples vary?
- ☐ Does the writing voice show understanding of the topic?
- ☐ Are the rules of capitalization followed?
- ☐ What changes could be made to improve the paragraph?

Name ______________________________ Date ______________

What is your vision of life in the future?

READING 3: From *The Time Warp Trio: 2095*

VOCABULARY **Literary Words** *Use with textbook page 413.*

REMEMBER **Science fiction** is writing that imagines what life will be like in the future. It often uses ideas from science and technology. **Setting** is the time and place where an event or story takes place. The setting can be real or make believe. Writers can tell you about the setting or give you clues in the story to figure it out.

Label each passage as *science fiction* or *setting*.

Literary Word	Example
setting	On a rainy November morning in 1776, a soldier walked up the dusty path in Virginia.
1.	It was a week before the Lhari ship went into warp drive, so Greg was bored. He felt glad when he saw the Juak medic coming to prepare him for cold-sleep.
2.	It is after dinner in January 1906, in the living room of Dr. Smith's house in London.
3.	It is 2007, in a small apartment in the back of a building in St. Louis.
4.	The creature had 16 arms and legs. It was green and slimy. It spoke in a creepy, high voice.
5.	Kea was going home to Pluto from school on Venus. "I'm glad the trip takes only an hour," she said as she put on her space suit.

Read the passage "Rebels of the Red Planet." Underline the words that show setting and circle words that imagine what life will be like in the future. The first example is done for you.

Rebels of the Red Planet

It was 5:00 P.M. The car bumped on the rocky road on Mars. The desert stretched to the distant horizon. It was silent and empty. The steel-blue sky shimmered above the red surface. The zeuzes made their odd noises as they flew backwards in the sky. The rebels adjusted their space suits, helmets, and oxygen tanks. Dark Kensington, more than 500 years old, decided that today he would overthrow the evil ruler who gripped the settlers on Mars.

VOCABULARY **Academic Words** *Use with textbook page 414.*

Read the paragraph below. Pay attention to the underlined academic words.

The goal of a persuasive speech is to shift the opinion of the listener. Successful speakers use a number of strategies to get and hold the attention of the listener. Common techniques include using catchy phrases, expressive body language, and the use of visuals. Good speeches also need to include a number of specific details about the subject, so that the listener believes the speaker is an expert.

Write the academic words from the paragraph above next to their correct definitions.

Example: ___*shift*___: a change in the way most people think about something, or in the way something is done

1. ________________: special methods of doing something
2. ________________: sets of plans and skills used in order to gain success or achieve an aim
3. ________________: detailed and exact

Use the academic words from the paragraph above to complete the sentences.

4. Her ________________ for getting to school on time are simple.
5. The teacher asked ________________ questions about the characters in the novel.
6. The artist uses the ________________ of dry brush and shading in her paintings.
7. I hope my school will ________________ its policy on lateness.

Complete the sentences with your own ideas.

Example: The athlete's strategies for winning include *getting a lot of sleep and drinking lots of water*.

8. I wish our library would shift its rules about ________________.
9. When my family travels, we usually have specific questions about ________________.
10. I think techniques for building future cities will include ________________.

Name ________________________________ Date ______________

WORD STUDY Schwa spelled *a, e, i, o, u* *Use with textbook page 415.*

REMEMBER The "uh" sound in a word is called a schwa. The symbol for the schwa is the letter *e* turned upside down. In multisyllabic words, the schwa occurs only in an unstressed syllable.
Example: In the word *lesson*, the schwa is in the second syllable.

Look at the words below. Say each word out loud. Circle the syllable that is stressed. Then, underline the schwa in each word.

pencil	about	cotton	confront	away
hurtful	sister	supply	utensil	broken

Write each word in the word box above in the chart below. Place each word under its correct column. Use a dictionary if needed.

Schwa spelled *e*	Schwa spelled *i*	Schwa spelled *o*	Schwa spelled *a*	Schwa spelled *u*

Write ten new words that have the schwa sound in an unstressed syllable. Circle the schwa. Use a dictionary if needed.

1. ____________ 6. ____________

2. ____________ 7. ____________

3. ____________ 8. ____________

4. ____________ 9. ____________

5. ____________ 10. ____________

READING STRATEGY **SKIM** *Use with textbook page 415.*

REMEMBER Before you read, skim the text to get a sense of what it is about. When you skim, you read the text quickly. Glance at the title, text and illustrations. Make predictiions about what you think the selection will be about.

Use the text to answer the questions that follow.

Homes of the Future

What will homes of the future look like? Will they even be on planet Earth or on another planet? Writers and artists love to imagine cities and homes of the future. Science fiction writers especially enjoy picturing homes of the future. Sometimes they envision houses that look like space ships. Other times, they imagine homes that are underwater or deep underground. New materials may make it possible to build extremely large homes very cheaply. It may be possible to live in a home that is woven from super strong carbon threads! One thing is for sure: if the homes of the future are anything like the way writers and artists picture them, life in the future is going to be very interesting.

1. Circle the title. What can you guess the article will be about from reading the title?

____

2. Circle the illustration. What does the illustration tell you about the content of the article?

____

3. Skim the text. What is the main idea of the text?

____

4. Predict what the text will be about.

____

5. How can the strategy of skimming help you to become an active reader?

____

Name ______________________________ Date ______________

COMPREHENSION

Use with textbook page 422.

Choose the best answer for each item. Circle the letter of the correct answer.

1. This story takes place in ______.

a. New York City **b.** Florida **c.** South America

2. *The Book* is important because it is ______.

a. a medical record **b.** filled with money **c.** a time-travel guide

3. The three boys and the three girls look alike because they ______.

a. wear the same clothing **b.** are the same age **c.** are related to each other

4. This story is ______.

a. serious **b.** funny **c.** scary

5. This story is science fiction because the characters ______.

a. can travel through time **b.** have a good time **c.** are all very smart

RESPONSE TO LITERATURE

Use with textbook page 423.

Imagine that you are Sam, Fred, and Joe. What can you do to solve your problem? Write at least five lines.

____

____

____

____

____

____

GRAMMAR End Punctuation, Commas, and Quotation Marks

Use with textbook page 424.

REMEMBER Use a period (.) to end a statement or an imperative; use a question mark (?) to end a question; use an exclamation point (!) to end a sentence that expresses strong feeling. Use a comma (,) to separate nouns or phrases in a series, to separate introductory words or phrases, and to set off a speaker's quoted words in a sentence. Quotation marks (" ") are used to set off a speaker's exact words.

Write the correct punctuation in the chart.

Comma	Period	Exclamation Point	Question Mark	Quotation Marks

Find the errors. Add one piece of punctuation to each sentence.

1. How do they do that
2. Wow I see it but I don't believe it.
3. There were people with green skin blue skin, and purple skin.
4. Come on Follow us.
5. "This is my room" said the girl.
6. "So you're not coming with us? I said.

Add the missing punctuation to this paragraph.

Sam Fred and Joe are three friends. They have traveled to the year 2095 Look closely said Sam. Everyone was floating a foot above the floor. Wow said Fred I see it but I don't believe it.

Name ______________________________ Date ______________

Parentheses, Brackets, and Ellipses *Use with textbook page 425.*

REMEMBER Parentheses (( )) are mainly used to show extra ideas. Brackets ([ ]) are used to show changes made to someone else's writing. Ellipses (...) are used when a word or phrase is missing from a statement.

Match the sentences with the explanations.

1. You wrote us a note . . . which I got from my mom. ______
2. Joe (the narrator) has a time-travel guide book. ______
3. As the story begins, [the three friends] are running away. ______

a. This is an extra idea added to the statement.
b. A change was made to this sentence.
c. A phrase is missing from this statement.

Rewrite the paragraph and make the following changes. Use parentheses, brackets, or ellipses to show your changes.

Instructions:

1. Add this information to explain "antigravity disks": a device that enables people to fly.
2. Change the words *the boys* to *Sam, Fred,* and *Joe.*
3. Add this information to explain "Sellbot": a kind of security robot.
4. Delete the words *who look strangely familiar.*
5. Change the words *the girls* (in the phrase "one of the girls") to *them.*
6. Delete the words *very much.*

Now wearing antigravity disks, the boys fly through the streets of New York, still chased by the Sellbot and three futuristic girls who look strangely familiar. Joe's uncle has appeared out of nowhere to help. The girls catch up, and Joe is surprised to see that one of the girls looks very much like his sister.

WRITING Include Quotations and Citations

Use with textbook pages 426–427.

Complete your own main idea/details web for a paragraph about time travel or science fiction.

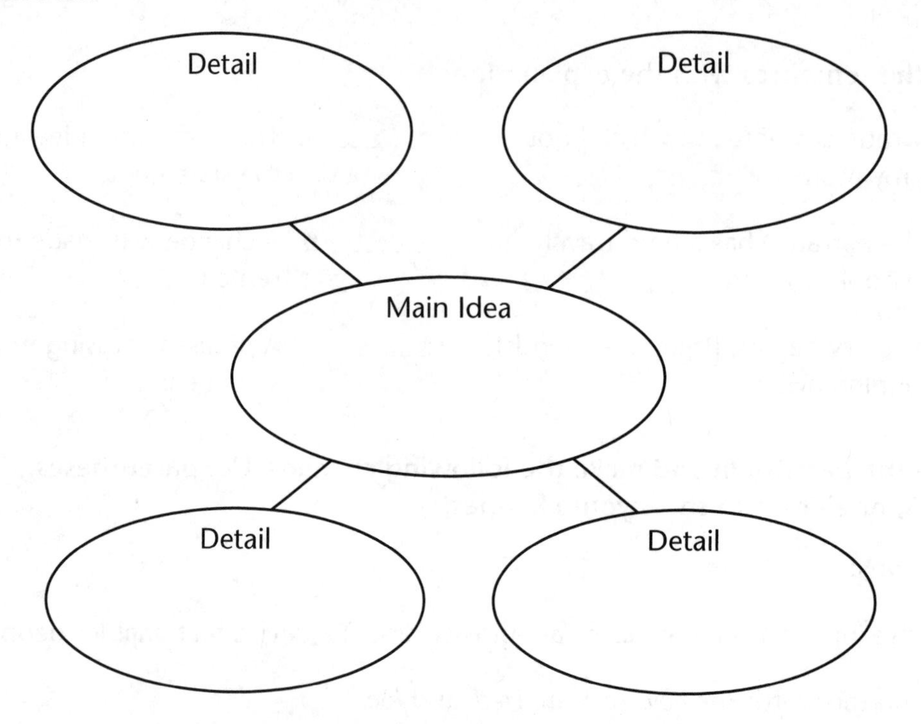

Use the Peer Review Checklist below to obtain feedback from your partner. This feedback will help you edit your final draft.

PEER REVIEW CHECKLIST

- ☐ Does the paragraph present a main idea?
- ☐ Does it include at least one quotation?
- ☐ Do all quotations support the main idea?
- ☐ Does every quotation include a citation?
- ☐ Are all citations accurate and complete?
- ☐ What changes could be made to improve the paragraph?

Name ______________________ Date ______________

What is your vision of life in the future?

READING 4: "NASA and the U.S. Space Program"

VOCABULARY **Key Words** *Use with textbook page 429.*

Write each word in the box next to its definition.

astronaut	historic	gravity	mission	NASA	simulation

Example: *simulation*: something you do or make in order to practice what you would do in a real situation

1. ______________: being important to a lot of people for a long time
2. ______________: the important aim in someone's work
3. ______________: someone who travels in space
4. ______________: a U.S. government organization that controls space travel and the scientific study of space
5. ______________: the force that makes objects fall to the ground

Use the words in the box at the top of the page to complete the sentences.

6. The two countries signed a ______________ peace agreement.
7. There is no ______________ in space.
8. Many different kinds of people work at ______________, but most of them studied science in college.
9. This year's space ______________ will go further and take longer than any of the others.
10. He is the youngest ______________ to ever walk on the moon.

VOCABULARY Academic Words *Use with textbook page 430.*

Read the paragraph below. Pay attention to the underlined Academic Words.

Every day brings a new challenge for my brother, who works for our state senator. He is in contact with important officials and plays a crucial role in helping his boss deal with controversy. His approach is always professional. Without his management skills, the staff wouldn't be able to function.

Write the letter of the correct definition next to each word.

Example: ___b___ controversy

_____ **1.** professional	**a.** work properly
_____ **2.** contact	**b.** a serious disagreement among many people over a plan, decision, etc., over a long period of time
_____ **3.** challenge	**c.** well trained and good at a job
_____ **4.** function	**d.** communication with a person, organization, or place
	e. something that tests your skill or ability

Use the academic words from above to complete the sentences.

5. It will be a ____________________ to learn how to ride a horse, so I am going to take lessons.

6. The ____________________ lasted for years. The two countries couldn't come to an agreement.

7. My cable television sometimes does not ____________________ well during bad wind or rain storms.

Complete the sentences with your own ideas.

Example: It was a big challenge for me to ___learn how to use my new computer___.

8. My biggest challenge in school is ____________________.

9. I like to stay in contact with ____________________.

10. My favorite professional athlete or musician is ____________________.

Name ______________________________ Date ______________

WORD STUDY Identifying Cognates *Use with textbook page 431.*

REMEMBER There are some words in English that look and sound almost the same as the word in Spanish. They also have the same meaning. We call these words cognates.

Choose the correct English spelling of each cognate.

1. futuro

a. futureo **b.** future

2. visión

a. vision **b.** vison

3. famoso

a. famos **b.** famous

4. diferente

a. differente **b.** different

5. momento

a. moment **b.** momenteo

Write the definition for each pair of cognates. Then use the English word in a sentence.

6. problema / problem ______________________________

____

7. equipo / equipment ______________________________

____

8. exploración / exploration ______________________________

____

9. programa / program ______________________________

____

READING STRATEGY EMPLOY ANALYTICAL SKILLS

Use with textbook page 431.

REMEMBER Using analytical skills will help you evaluate a writer's purpose and argument, distinguish facts from opinions, and decide whether or not you agree with the writer's position.

Read the following passage and answer the questions that follow.

Editorial: DNA and Justice

Since the 1980s, forensic scientists have used DNA fingerprints to investigate and solve crimes. They take a sample of blood, hair, or other body tissue found at the scene of a crime. This tissue contains DNA. Scientists check to see whether the DNA from a crime scene matches a sample of the suspect's DNA.

In recent years, thanks to organizations such as the Innocence Project, many people have been released from prison after DNA tests proved that they were innocent. On June 18, 2009, the U.S. Supreme Court ruled by a 5-to-4 decision that prisoners have *no constitutional right* to DNA testing that might prove their innocence if they were wrongfully convicted. The Court decided this is a state issue, not a federal one. This decision will hurt innocent prisoners as well as victims of crimes. As of 2009, more than 240 people previously convicted of serious crimes have been found innocent because of DNA testing. Out of those 240 cases, 103 *real* criminals were convicted based on their DNA.

Some people say that a DNA test is too expensive to give to every prisoner who asks for it. But what about the $20,000 it costs taxpayers to maintain each prisoner for one year? And what about the cost to a wrongly convicted person—how can we repay the years stolen from them and their families? DNA testing should be a constitutional right for *all* people convicted of a crime who believe that DNA testing will prove their innocence. Everyone must have access to the technology so that we as a nation stop wrongful convictions and give crime victims the satisfaction of knowing that the right person is behind bars.

1. What is the writer's purpose for writing this text? What issue or controversy is presented?

____

____

2. What is the most important idea in the text? _______________

____

3. Underline the main facts in red. Underline the writer's opinions in blue.

4. Does the writer provide enough evidence to convince you? Why or why not?

____

____

Name ______________________________ Date ______________

COMPREHENSION

Use with textbook page 436.

Choose the best answer for each item. Circle the letter of the correct answer.

1. Visitors to the Johnson Space Center learn ______.

   a. only what astronauts do
   b. only what scientists do
   c. what both astronauts and scientists do

2. The atmosphere in space is ______.

   a. the same as the atmosphere on Earth
   b. colder with less air than Earth
   c. warmer with less air than Earth

3. Astronauts have to learn to move while floating, which is to move ______.

   a. slowly through the air
   b. quickly through the air
   c. slowly on the ground

4. Mission control specialists help astronauts ______.

   a. only before a space launch
   b. only during a space launch
   c. both before and during a space launch

5. Today, the equipment in the NASA control center is ______ than it was in the past.

   a. bigger and better
   b. smaller and better
   c. bigger and more expensive

EXTENSION

Use with textbook page 437.

Many books, TV shows, and movies are about space exploration and travel. Write a paragraph about a book, TV show, or movie that you know about space. Describe the plot, and tell if you like it and why.

____

____

____

____

____

____

____

Name _______________

GRAMMAR Using Quotation Marks for Exact Words

Use with textbook page 438.

REMEMBER When writing dialogue, or a conversation, in a narrative, enclose a character's exact words or thoughts in quotation marks. In expository writing, place quotation marks around a person's exact words when you are quoting them. For long quotations, use a block quotation. A block quotation is indented, single-spaced, and not enclosed in quotation marks.

Write a ✓ next to each sentence that uses quotation marks correctly.

1. _______ "He said, Come to my house for dinner."

   _______ He said, "Come to my house for dinner."

2. _______ "Please forgive me!" she pleaded.

   _______ "Please forgive me! she pleaded.

3. _______ "You are a good friend," said Rita.

   _______ You are a good friend, "said Rita."

4. _______ She said, Listen to me carefully.

   _______ She said, "Listen to me carefully."

Add quotation marks to each sentence.

5. Do you want to travel into space? asked the guide.
6. The boy asked, Can we visit the mission control center?
7. I want to be an astronaut one day, she said.
8. Let's go and see inside the Space Shuttle, he said.

Name ______________________________ Date ______________

Quotation Marks: Terms, Expressions, and Titles

Use with textbook page 439.

REMEMBER Use quotation marks to enclose special or unfamiliar terms and any other unusual expressions. Use quotation marks to set off a word or phrase that defines another word or phrase. Use quotation marks to set off a title of a short written work such as articles, poems, and short stories.

Write a ✓ next to each sentence that uses quotation marks correctly.

1. ______ Romeo and Juliet was written by "Shakespeare."

______ "Romeo and Juliet" was written by Shakespeare.

2. ______ "DNA" stands for deoxyribonucleic acid.

______ DNA stands for "deoxyribonucleic acid."

3. ______ "Mending Wall" is a poem by Robert Frost.

______ "Mending Wall is a poem by Robert Frost.

4. ______ They used a "lunar module," a vehicle designed to explore the moon.

______ They used a lunar module, "a vehicle designed to explore the moon."

Add quotation marks to these sentences.

5. Have you read The Raven by Edgar Allan Poe?

6. DNA is known as your genetic fingerprint.

7. Ray Bradbury wrote the book Fahrenheit 451.

8. MRI stands for magnetic resonance imaging.

9. I read an article called Life on Mars.

WRITING Include Paraphrases and Citations

Use with textbook pages 440–441.

Complete your own main idea/details web for a paragraph about a science topic.

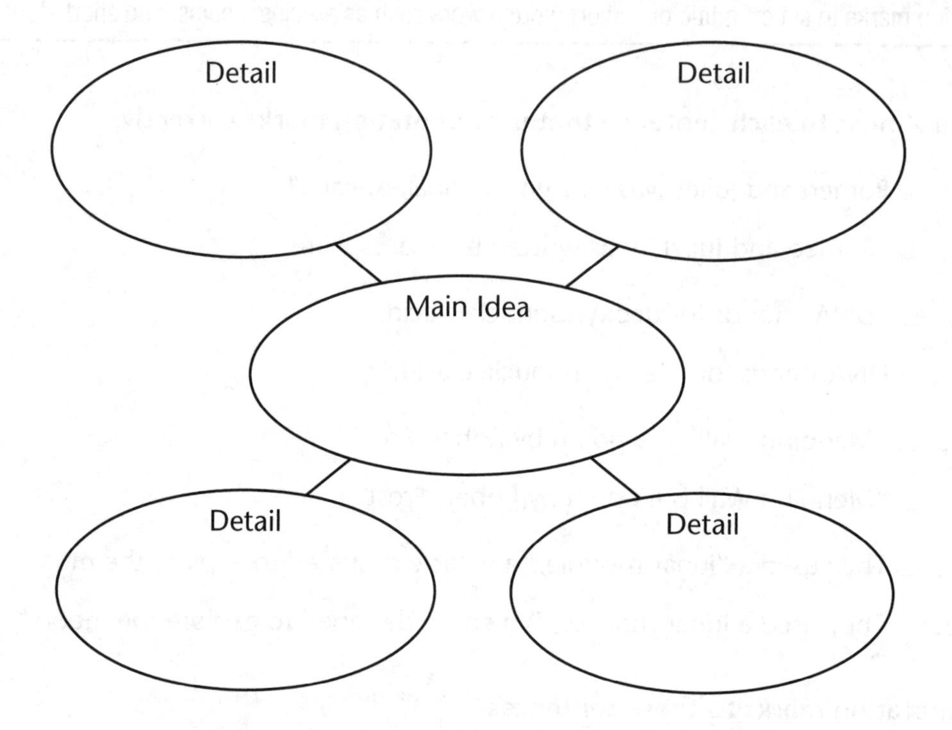

Use the Peer Review Checklist below to obtain feedback from your partner. This feedback will help you edit your final draft.

PEER REVIEW CHECKLIST

- ☐ Does the paragraph present a main idea?
- ☐ Does the main idea focus on a topic related to science?
- ☐ Does the writer paraphrase information from a source?
- ☐ Are citations included for all paraphrases and quotations?
- ☐ Are quotation marks used correctly?
- ☐ What changes could be made to improve the paragraph?

Name ____________________ Date ____________

WRITING WORKSHOP *Use with textbook pages 446–451.*

Organize your ideas in the graphic organizer below.

I. ____________________
  A. ____________________
  B. ____________________
II. ____________________
  A. ____________________
  B. ____________________
III. ____________________
  A. ____________________
  B. ____________________
IV. ____________________
  A. ____________________
  B. ____________________
V. ____________________
  A. ____________________
  B. ____________________

Use the Peer Review Checklist below to obtain feedback from your partner. This feedback will help you edit your final draft.

PEER REVIEW CHECKLIST

- ☐ Does the report provide good information and explanations?
- ☐ Does it use strong quotations to support some of the main ideas?
- ☐ Was the organization of facts and details easy to follow?
- ☐ Does the writer spell words correctly?
- ☐ Is there a complete list of sources at the end of the report?
- ☐ What changes could be made to improve the essay?

LEARNING LOG *Use after completing page 452.*

Underline the vocabulary items you know and can use well. Review and practice any you haven't underlined. Underline them when you know them well.

Literary Words	Key Words	Academic Words	
simile metaphor stanzas science fiction setting	artificial canyons frontier mass-produced robots volcanoes astronaut gravity historic mission NASA simulation	function occupation research trend complex interpretation published section shift specific strategies techniques	challenge contact controversy crucial function professional

Put a check by the skills you can perform well. Review and practice any you haven't checked off. Check them off when you can perform them well.

Skills	I can . . .
Word Study	☐ recognize and spell diphthongs /oi/ and /ou/. ☐ recognize Greek and Latin roots. ☐ recognize and pronounce the schwa spelled a, e, i, o, u. ☐ identify and use cognates.
Reading Strategies	☐ take notes. ☐ analyze text structure. ☐ skim. ☐ employ analytical skills.
Grammar	☐ use transitions. ☐ recognize rules of capitalization. ☐ use punctuation. ☐ use quotation marks.
Writing	☐ write an introductory paragraph. ☐ support a main idea with examples. ☐ include quotations and citations. ☐ include paraphrases and citations. ☐ write a research report.

TEST 1

DIRECTIONS
Read this selection. Then answer the questions that follow it.

Telephones Then and Now

1 Telephones have changed a lot in recent years. The first telephone my family had was connected to a wall in the house. Wires in the house connected to telephone wires outside. The sound was carried over the wires until it finally made it to my friend's house. Even if you had a long cord, it was still difficult to move around the room while you were talking.

2 The next telephone we had was still connected to the wall. But the receiver had a battery, and you could walk around the house while you called your friend. You could dial the number, speak, and listen using the mobile receiver. You still had to put the receiver in its base when you were finished talking so that it could be charged.

3 My mom recently bought a new phone. This phone does just about everything! She can use it to surf the Internet and send e-mails. She can even check her social networking page. She doesn't even need to use the number keys any more. Mom can just touch the application on the screen with her finger, and the phone does the rest. Most importantly, the phone isn't connected to anything unless it is time to charge it. You can take it almost anywhere.

1 Today's telephones are ______.

A able to do many things
B connected to a wire
C only available to the rich
D available in many styles

2 What is one thing Mom cannot do with her new phone?

F Send e-mail
G Surf the Internet
H Check her social networking page
J Mail a package

TEST 2

DIRECTIONS
Read this selection. Then answer the questions that follow it.

What Would You Like to Be?

1 Lee's teacher wrote a question on the board. The question was "What would you like your life to be like twenty years from now?"

2 Lee had to think about the question. It was a hard one, but he had an idea. Last week, he had read a book about Jane Goodall. Jane Goodall is a scientist. She spent thirty-five years studying chimpanzees. She saw that chimpanzees made tools out of plants and used these tools to catch insects for food. Before this discovery, scientists thought only humans made and used tools. Jane Goodall had learned something important for science.

3 Lee smiled as he wrote his answer to the question: *In twenty years, I want to be a scientist like Jane Goodall. I want to study animals and find out what they eat, how they find their food, how they make their homes, and how they teach their young to survive. I want to make an important discovery about animals.*

1 What is paragraph 3 mainly about?

- **A** The assignment the teacher wrote on the board
- **B** What Lee wants his life to be like in twenty years
- **C** How Lee wants to make an important discovery
- **D** Jane Goodall's discoveries about chimpanzees

2 According to the selection, Lee wants to —

- **F** study chimpanzees with Jane Goodall
- **G** learn how chimpanzees use tools
- **H** discover something important about animals
- **J** find out what kinds of insects chimpanzees eat

3 What does the word *survive* mean?

- **A** find food
- **B** build a home
- **C** stay alive
- **D** make a discovery

4 According to the selection, what can the reader conclude about Lee?

- **F** He likes art.
- **G** He is interested in science.
- **H** He wants to be a teacher.
- **J** He likes school.

Name ______________________________ Date ______________

TEST 3

DIRECTIONS
Read this selection. Then answer the questions that follow it.

Martin Luther King, Jr.

1 "I have a dream," Martin Luther King, Jr. said in his most famous speech. His dream was that some day all people would have equal rights. He inspired people to come together to fight for this dream. King worked to make sure that African Americans would get the same rights as other people. He believed the best way to make the government change was through nonviolence. He did not want people to use force in their protests. King was a great leader who changed history.

2 Martin Luther King, Jr. lived in the southern part of the United States. During this time, African Americans had to sit at the back of the bus. If a bus was crowded, African Americans had to give their seats to white bus riders. One day, an African American woman named Rosa Parks refused to give up her seat. She was arrested. King convinced African Americans in the city to stop using the city buses in protest. Their protest lasted more than a year, but afterwards African Americans could sit anywhere on the buses.

3 After those events, King led many marches and protests. He was even sent to jail because of his work. But he knew he couldn't give up. He had to fight for a future in which all people were equal.

4 When King led an important march in Washington, D.C. and said, "I have a dream," people listened to him. Changes began to happen. The government passed a law saying that all people, no matter what race they are, have equal rights to jobs and houses.

5 Not everyone agreed with King. Some people didn't want anything to change. Some people wanted change to happen faster. But King continued to do the work he believed in until he was killed in 1968. King will always be important to Americans because he believed in equal rights for all people.

1 Look at this graphic organizer.

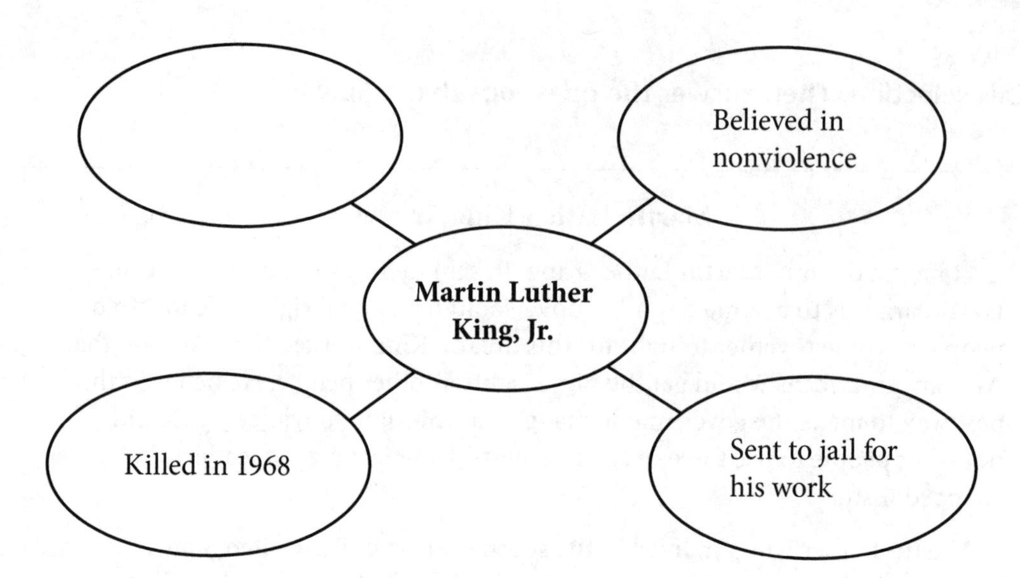

Look at this web about Martin Luther King, Jr. What information best completes the web?

A Believed in equal rights for all people
B Refused to give up his seat on a bus
C Wanted change to happen faster
D Believed in using violence

2 Paragraph 2 is mainly about —

F how King helped change bus laws
G how bus drivers treated riders
H how King used nonviolence
J how people listened to King

3 In paragraph 1, what words help the reader know what *nonviolence* means?

A make the government
B change government
C use force
D equal rights

4 According to the article, how did King help change bus laws?

F He asked the government to change the laws.
G He refused to give up his seat on a bus.
H He convinced African Americans to stop using the buses.
J He was arrested for not moving to the back of the bus.

5 Which sentence from the selection explains King's beliefs?

A *His dream was that some day all people would have equal rights.*
B *He was even sent to jail because of his work.*
C *King convinced African Americans in the city to stop using the city buses in protest.*
D *King will always be important to Americans because he believed in equal rights for all people.*

Name ______________________________ Date ______________

Visual Literacy: Smithsonian American Art Museum

Use with textbook pages 454–455.

LEARNING TO LOOK

Look at *Sculpture Group Symbolizing World's Communication in the Atomic Age* by Harry Bertoia on page 455 in your textbook. Describe six things you see in this artwork. State facts, not opinions.

Example: *star*

1. ______________________
2. ______________________
3. ______________________
4. ______________________
5. ______________________
6. ______________________

INTERPRETATION

Look at *San Francisco to New York in One Hour* by Alexander Maldonado on page 454 in your textbook. Imagine you are in this painting. Describe the scene.

Example: *I am in a car inside the tube. It is going very fast . . .*

What are you doing?

____

____

____

____

Where are you going?

____

____

____

____

5W&H

Look at *San Francisco to New York in One Hour* by Alexander Maldonado on page 454 in your textbook. Imagine you could interview the artist about his painting. What would you ask him? Use *Who, What, Why, Where, When* and *How* to frame your questions.

Example: Why *did you choose this title for the painting?*

1. **Who** ______________________________

____

2. **What** ______________________________

____

3. **Why** ______________________________

____

4. **Where** ______________________________

____

5. **When** ______________________________

____

6. **How** ______________________________

____

Editing and Proofreading Marks

To:	Use This Mark	Example:
add something	∧	We ate rice, bean∧ and corn. (s)
delete something	℘	We ate rice, beans, and corns.
close space	⁀	We ⁀ ate rice, beans, and corn.
start a new paragraph	¶	¶ We ate rice, beans, and corn.
add a comma	∧	We ate rice, beans∧ and corn.
add a period	⊙	We ate rice, beans, and corn⊙
switch letters or words	∽	We ate rice, baens, and corn.
change to a capital letter	≡	we ate rice, beans, and corn.
change to a lowercase letter	/	WE ate rice, beans, and corn.
let the marked text stand	(stet)	We ate rice, beans, and corn. (stet)